British
English

Personal Best

Workbook

B1
Pre-intermediate

Series Editor
Jim Scrivener

Authors
Elizabeth Walter
and **Kate Woodford**

Richmond

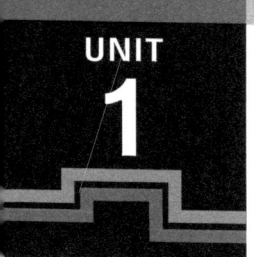

UNIT 1

All about me

1A LANGUAGE

GRAMMAR: Present simple and adverbs of frequency

1 Order the words to complete the sentences.

1 meets / her friend Petra / sometimes
Gloria _____ for coffee.

2 hardly ever / the bus / catches
Daniel _____ to work.

3 cycle / you / often
Do _____ to the office?

4 never / any / does
Miguel _____ housework.

5 listen / to / often
We _____ the radio.

6 visit / always / my friend
I _____ at the weekend.

7 see / she / does / often
How _____ Mehmet?

8 study / usually / don't
They _____ in the morning.

9 to / sometimes / goes
Silvia _____ the theatre.

10 usually / eat / doesn't
Ayesha _____ breakfast.

2 Complete the sentences with the correct form of the verbs in brackets.

1 Greta _____ two brothers. (have)

2 Paul _____ his hair every day. (wash)

3 My friend Enrico _____ in a factory. (work)

4 Marta and Luis _____ in Buenos Aires – they live in Brasília. (not live)

5 _____ you _____ Portuguese? (speak)

6 Ben _____ to America every summer to visit his family. (fly)

7 We _____ swimming. (not like)

8 _____ they _____ to the same school as you? (go)

VOCABULARY: Personality adjectives

3 Match descriptions 1–8 with adjectives a–h.

1 Anna often says things that upset other people. _____
2 Ed's always buying presents for his friends. _____
3 Pablo hardly ever laughs. _____
4 Terri doesn't like meeting new people. _____
5 The children always remember to say please and thank you. _____
6 George tells lies and tricks people. _____
7 Dad goes to the office at weekends! _____
8 My Maths teacher explains things carefully and never gets angry. _____

a serious
b hard-working
c shy
d dishonest
e polite
f unkind
g patient
h generous

4 Complete the adjectives.

1 My brother is a really im_____ person – he hates queueing in shops.

2 Lola is so se_____ – she only thinks about herself.

3 You can believe everything that Julia tells you – she's a very ho_____ person.

4 Ricardo never says hello to my parents when he comes to our house. They think he's r_____.

5 Marc is very so_____ – he has lots of friends and often has parties at his flat.

6 Hannah is so f_____ – I never stop laughing when I'm with her.

7 Dan often helps me with jobs I need to do. He's very k_____.

8 Maria's so l_____ – she stays in bed most of the day at weekends!

PRONUNCIATION: Final *-s/-es* sound

5 ▶1.1 Listen to the verb endings in these sentences. Tick (✔) the correct column.

	/s/	/z/	/ɪz/
1 He <u>wants</u> to be a doctor.			
2 Silvia <u>goes</u> to college.			
3 Aisha <u>likes</u> chocolate.			
4 Ana <u>watches</u> TV in the evening.			
5 Paulo <u>changes</u> clothes twice a day.			
6 Adam <u>knows</u> my brother.			
7 Leila <u>thinks</u> football is boring.			
8 Mr Jones <u>teaches</u> us French.			

LISTENING: Listening for the main idea

1 ▶1.2 Listen to Daniel and Laura's conversation. Are the sentences about Daniel true (T) or false (F)?

1 He wants to stop using his mobile phone for a few weeks. _____

2 He wants to use his free time differently. _____

3 He wants to spend less time with other people. _____

4 He goes to the cinema a lot. _____

5 He wants to go out more. _____

6 He doesn't want to spend any time in the kitchen. _____

2 ▶1.2 Complete the sentences with the correct contractions then listen again and check.

1 So, Daniel, I hear you _____ using your phone this month.

2 At least, when _____ not at work.

3 I realized that I _____ actually do anything these days.

4 We never go out together these days. I mean, _____ crazy.

5 I _____ live my life like this!

6 I watch films at home on my laptop instead. It _____ good.

7 Oh, and my _____ staying with me at the moment.

8 _____ really good at baking.

3 Complete the sentences with the verbs in the box. There are two extra verbs.

keep   collect   play   go on   shop
bake   do   go out   spend   meet up with

1 He wants to _____ more time with his family.

2 She goes running three times a week to _____ fit.

3 Do you often _____ your friends after work?

4 Some of the kids _____ chess at lunchtime.

5 In our spare time we like to _____ cakes.

6 Do your parents _____ much exercise?

7 I don't _____ social media much.

8 They don't go to the supermarket. They prefer to _____ online.

GRAMMAR: Present continuous and present simple

1 Choose the correct options to complete the sentences.

1 Kati can't go out today. ____ her essay.
   a She's finishing   b She finishes

2 This soup is very salty. ____ it.
   a I'm not liking   b I don't like

3 ____ a lot in your country?
   a Is it snowing   b Does it snow

4 ____ for our exams at the moment.
   a We're studying   b We study

5 Is that Emir? ____ his brother.
   a I'm knowing   b I know

6 Sophia is busy. ____ dinner.
   a She's cooking   b She cooks

7 Luis works as a journalist. ____ articles about sport.
   a He's writing   b He writes

8 I can go with you. ____ anything at the moment.
   a I'm not doing   b I don't do

9 ____ his daughter to school every morning.
   a Sam is taking   b Sam takes

10 ____ to the gym with you very often?
   a Is Raul going   b Does Raul go

2 Complete the sentences with the present simple or present continuous form of the verbs in the box.

> think   not play   walk   do
> come from   work   wear   have

1 Mr Silva _____ past our house every morning.

2 Mum and Dad _____ their lunch at the moment.

3 Laura _____ in a café for three months this summer.

4 Luca _____ football very often.

5 Olga and Sergei _____ Russia.

6 _____ Helen usually _____ her homework in the evenings?

7 Maria _____ that our new teacher is great.

8 Jorge _____ a jacket today.

VOCABULARY: Useful verbs

3 Choose the correct verbs to complete the sentences.

1 I often ____ my keys – it's so annoying!   miss   lose

2 Pablo usually ____ our swimming races.   wins   earns

3 Susie ____ really happy, doesn't she?   looks like   looks

4 I'm cold! Let's ____ home.   go back   come back

5 Emma's ____ a blue coat today.   wearing   carrying

6 Can you ____ me to call Ali later?   remember   remind

7 I'm ____ for Francesca to arrive.   hoping   waiting

8 Are you ____ your holiday?   looking forward to   expecting

9 Emma often ____ me about her friends.   says   tells

10 I need to ____ some documents to Mr Smith's office.   take   bring

4 Complete the conversation with verbs from exercise 3 in the correct tense.

Ana Are you going to Jorge and Sara's wedding? I'm really [1]_____ it.

Laura Yes, I am! But I can only buy them a small present, because I'm not [2]_____ very much money at the moment.

Ana Never mind! Do you have something to wear to the wedding?

Laura No, but my sister [3]_____ from holiday tomorrow and she has so many amazing dresses.

Ana I [4]_____ she has something suitable then!

Laura Yes, definitely. Every week she [5]_____ home something new from the shops!

Ana By the way, do you [6]_____ Carlos, Jorge's best friend?

Laura Yes, I do. He's the tall guy that [7]_____ Zac Efron, isn't he? He's great – I really [8]_____ he'll be at the wedding.

Ana Of course he will. Jorge [9]_____ that he's like a brother to him. He works in France in the winter, and Jorge really [10]_____ him when he's away.

PRONUNCIATION: -ng sound

5 ▶1.3 Practise saying the sentences. Listen, check and repeat.

1 I'm bri**ng**ing Julio to the meeti**ng**.

2 He's studyi**ng** French at university.

3 She's carryi**ng** a you**ng** child.

4 Are they runni**ng** in the park?

5 They're singi**ng** my favourite so**ng**.

6 I'm taki**ng** a stro**ng** box for the heavy books.

7 She's weari**ng** a lo**ng** dress.

WRITING: Making notes

1 Read Cristina's blog about three important people in her life. Number the information for each person in the order it appears.

Bianca:
a personality ____
b relationship to Cristina ____
c age ____

Clara Fuentes:
a how she helped Cristina ____
b her job ____
c relationship to Cristina ____

Granddad:
a personality ____
b relationship to Cristina's father ____
c lifestyle ____

Lots of people say that their brothers and sisters are annoying, but I love being with my sister, Bianca. That's probably ¹_____ I don't live with her all the time! I'm away at university, but she's only six, ²_____ our relationship is a bit different from most sisters. Bianca's really funny, and she makes me laugh a lot. When we go out, people sometimes think I'm her mum. I hope I have a daughter like her one day – but not yet!

The second person who is very important to me is my neighbour, Clara Fuentes. She has quite an unusual job for a woman ³_____ she's an airline pilot. Clara told me once that women can do any job in the world! ⁴_____ I'm studying engineering. There are only three women on my course, but I love it and I'm good at it.

Person number three is my granddad, who is my dad's father. My dad has five brothers. ⁵_____ our family is so big! Granddad lives alone, but we all visit him, ⁶_____ he's never lonely! He is interested in all of us, and always wants to know about our lives. He's very kind and generous and everyone loves him.

2 Complete 1–6 in the blog with *because, so* or *That's why* and decide if each one is a reason or result.

3 Think of three important people in your life. Write notes about them.

Person 1	
name	
relationship to you	
their life: job, where they live, etc.	
their personality	
why they are important to you	

Person 2	
name	
relationship to you	
their life: job, where they live, etc.	
their personality	
why they are important to you	

Person 3	
name	
relationship to you	
their life: job, where they live, etc.	
their personality	
why they are important to you	

4 Write a blog about three important people in your life.

- Use some or all of your notes from exercise 3.
- Write as many ideas as you can about the main topics.
- Choose the best ideas and organize them into paragraphs.
- Include at least three sentences with *because, so* or *That's why*.

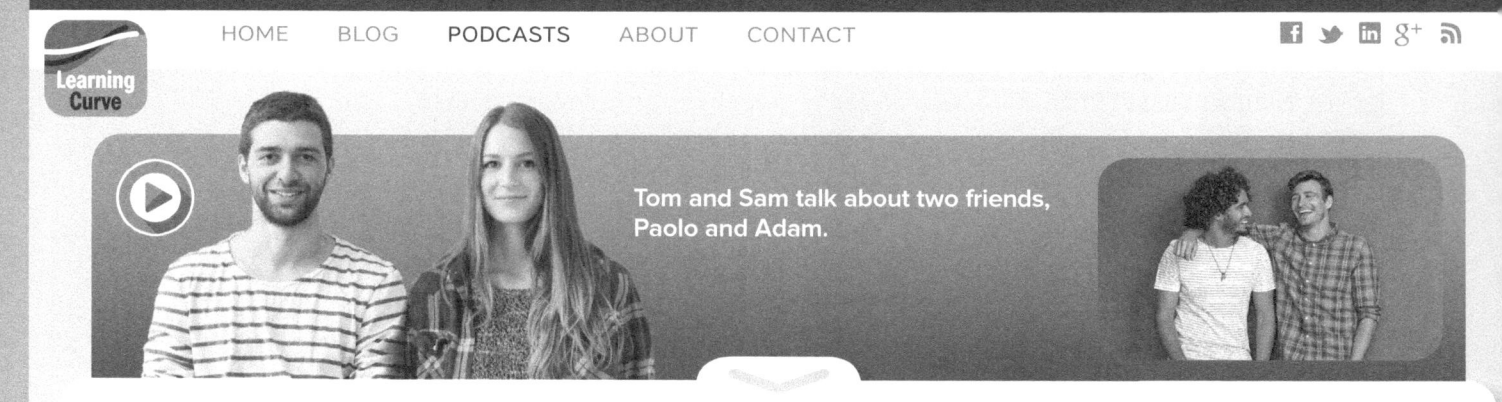

Tom and Sam talk about two friends, Paolo and Adam.

LISTENING

1 ▶1.4 Listen to the podcast. Tick (✔) the things Paolo talks about.

a Adam's hobbies _____

b how he met Adam _____

c Adam's personality _____

d what he has in common with Adam _____

e Adam's children _____

f where Paolo lives _____

2 ▶1.4 Listen again. Choose the correct options to complete the sentences.

1 Paolo regularly sees Adam
  a most evenings.
  b when they go running.
  c at work.

2 Paolo says that Adam
  a enjoys going out.
  b has a lot of friends.
  c isn't very sociable.

3 Adam spends some of his free time
  a playing with his sons.
  b doing sport with his sons.
  c teaching his sons Spanish.

4 Paolo and Adam
  a often go to concerts with each other.
  b belong to the same gym.
  c like different types of music.

5 Paolo says that Adam
  a never talks about his friends.
  b does the same job as Paolo.
  c helps Paolo with his problems.

6 Adam
  a is usually very serious.
  b makes Paolo laugh.
  c can sometimes be selfish.

READING

1 Read the blog about friendship. Tick (✔) the correct sentences.

a Teresa and Livia are about the same age. _____

b Teresa and Livia have different jobs. _____

c Teresa and Livia both have children. _____

d Teresa isn't married. _____

e Livia is Teresa's only friend. _____

2 Are the sentences true (T), false (F) or is there not enough information to decide (N)?

1 According to the writer, nobody can be friends with someone who is 25 years older. _____

2 Teresa and Livia work in the same place. _____

3 They often spend time together. _____

4 Teresa thinks that Livia gets tired more often than her. _____

5 Teresa has a lot of problems with her children. _____

6 Teresa discusses all her problems with her mother, too. _____

7 Teresa and Livia always like the same books. _____

8 Teresa learns more from Livia than Livia learns from Teresa. _____

9 Livia always likes the clothes that Teresa suggests for her. _____

10 Livia enjoys going out with Teresa. _____

HOME   BLOG   PODCASTS   ABOUT   CONTACT

Sam writes about friendship.

What's 25 years between friends?

What do you think of when you hear or use the phrase 'best friend'? Probably two people of around the same age. When we think of relationships between older and younger people, we may feel more negative about them. How often do we hear old people complaining that the young are lazy, selfish and rude? Or young people saying that the old don't understand them? But does it have to be like that? Teresa Fuentes, 28 and Livia Robles, 53 say that it doesn't!

Teresa

Livia and I work together in a large secondary school. She works in the school office, and I'm a History teacher. We usually have lunch together, and sometimes we go out in the evening, too. Livia may be 25 years older than me, but she's so much fun, and sometimes I think she has more energy than me! That's probably because I'm looking after three small children, and her children are grown up.

I love having an older friend, because Livia is always patient and she has a lot of life experience. She's interested in my life and gives me lots of good advice, especially about the kids. She's not afraid to be honest if she thinks I'm doing something wrong. I often talk to her about things I can't discuss with my mum because I don't want to worry her. But to me, Livia isn't like another mother – she's just Livia, my friend!

Livia

I think it's a really good thing to have friends of all ages. Talking to people with different lives and different experiences makes you think about things in a new way. Teresa and I often discuss books we're reading and it's interesting how different our opinions can be!

Teresa says she learns from me, but I learn a lot from her, too – about things like cooking and gardening. She and her husband grow all their own vegetables! She loves fashion too, and often suggests things for me that I wouldn't choose myself. This pink jacket I'm wearing now, for example.

And having a friend in her twenties means that I can go out and have fun. She even takes me to clubs sometimes! Being with Teresa and her friends reminds me of being young, and anyway, there's a lot more to life than housework and watching TV!

Stories and pictures

2A — **LANGUAGE**

GRAMMAR: Past simple and time expressions

1 Order the letters to make the past simple form of the verbs.

1 Anna usually cycles to work, but today she **kedlaw** _____.

2 Daniel **okot** _____ a train to college yesterday.

3 Last night Marta **newt** _____ to a concert.

4 Did you **grinb** _____ any money with you?

5 We **ederbmerem** _____ to send Tim a birthday card.

6 I **rited** _____ to open the door, but it was locked.

7 Beatriz **retow** _____ him a letter to explain the problem.

8 I **dretsta** _____ my new job in January.

9 We **beldimc** _____ to the top of the mountain.

10 Sara **tens** _____ me an email with the details.

2 Complete Rafael's postcard with the past simple of the verbs in brackets.

Hi Mum and Dad!

We ¹ _____ (get) here safely yesterday. The journey ² _____ (be) fine. Daniel's dad ³ _____ (meet) us at the airport and ⁴ _____ (drive) us to their house. In the evening we ⁵ _____ (go) to a movie. On the way, we ⁶ _____ (stop) at a café and ⁷ _____ (have) some pizza. We ⁸ _____ (come) home after midnight – I'm so tired today!

Love from Rafael

VOCABULARY: -ed/-ing adjectives

3 Complete 1–6 with an adjective from each pair in the box.

> amazed / amazing   annoyed / annoying   excited / exciting
> confused / confusing   interested / interesting   tired / tiring

1 I'm _____ by these instructions. They're not very clear.

2 My neighbours are _____ – they're so noisy.

3 Esra's brother is very _____ in cars.

4 She's so _____ about her holiday. She's really looking forward to it.

5 Paolo felt _____ after running ten kilometres.

6 We went to a fantastic restaurant last night – the food was _____!

4 Complete the sentences with -ed or -ing adjectives.

1 I often fall asleep in my Maths lessons. They're so b_____!

2 Bruna was di_____ when she failed her driving test.

3 I'm su_____ to see Manuel. He doesn't usually come here.

4 Cristina's really fr_____ of snakes, but her sister's not scared of them.

5 It's so em_____ when you can't remember someone's name!

6 We love spending the day at the beach – it's very re_____.

PRONUNCIATION: -ed endings

5 ▶ 2.1 Listen and circle the sound that you hear at the end of the underlined verb. Listen, check and repeat.

1	We <u>climbed</u> to the top of the mountain.	/t/	/ɪd/	/d/
2	I <u>decided</u> to go to Murilo's house.	/t/	/ɪd/	/d/
3	Eduardo <u>looked</u> at the photograph.	/t/	/ɪd/	/d/
4	The cook <u>experimented</u> with new dishes.	/t/	/ɪd/	/d/
5	I <u>travelled</u> to Rome by train.	/t/	/ɪd/	/d/
6	In the evening, we <u>watched</u> TV.	/t/	/ɪd/	/d/
7	We <u>opened</u> our presents together.	/t/	/ɪd/	/d/
8	She <u>worked</u> all day yesterday.	/t/	/ɪd/	/d/

READING: Approaching a text

1 Read the title and the first three lines of the text. What do you think it is about?

a A man who doesn't say much.

b A man who isn't as quiet as people think.

c A man who shouts a lot.

2 Look at the photograph. Who do you think the people are?

3 Match topics 1–4 with paragraph headings A–D.

1 A shy person doing something brave. _____

2 A couple getting married. _____

3 Something that is written down. _____

4 People wondering what someone will do. _____

Robyn Jones thought her grandfather was a quiet, shy man. Then she read her grandmother's diary and learned about the one time he wasn't …

A **All in black and white**

Granny's diary was for the year 1950. Every day she wrote about her life. Before June, it was mostly about her job in a jewellery shop and the lives of the other young women who worked there. But after June, she started to mention a regular customer – a nice young man who came in to buy a necklace for his mother, and then came the next day, and the next, and the next …

B **Will he, won't he?**

Each time, he asked Granny to help him, but he never bought anything else. Eventually, one of the other assistants said to Granny, 'I know why he comes. It's to see you!' They all expected Granddad to ask her out, but he never did.

C **The mouse becomes a lion**

Then one day, everything changed. Granddad was in the shop when a man ran in with a gun. He pointed it at Granny and told her to give him a diamond ring. In an instant, that shy young man changed. 'Drop the gun!' he shouted, and pushed the man to the floor. 'Don't you dare frighten that young woman! She's going to be my wife one day!'

The quiet man?

D **Wedding bells**

After that, the police came and arrested the robber, and everyone said that Granddad was a hero. But there was something Granny still wasn't sure about. 'Did you just ask me to marry you?' she asked Granddad. Granddad just smiled, but two months later they got married!

4 Are the sentences true (T) or false (F)?

1 Granny wrote about Granddad before June. _____

2 Granddad bought lots of jewellery from the shop. _____

3 The other assistants thought Granddad liked Granny. _____

4 The robber tried to steal a necklace from the shop. _____

5 Granddad was very angry with the robber. _____

6 The police took the robber away. _____

7 The people in the shop thought Granddad was brave. _____

8 Granny already knew that Granddad wanted to marry her. _____

5 Complete the sentences about the text with *then*, *after* or *later*.

1 _____ Robyn Jones read her grandmother's diary, she had a different idea about her grandfather.

2 One day, Granddad came to the shop to buy a necklace. A day _____, he came into the shop again.

3 _____ that, Granny started to write about him in her diary.

4 _____ a while, another shop assistant realized that Granddad was coming to see Granny.

5 A man pointed a gun at Granny. _____ he tried to steal a ring.

6 A few minutes _____, the police arrived.

GRAMMAR: Question forms

1 Order the words to make questions.

1 did / do / what / on holiday / they

_____?

2 need / we / to buy / do / a ticket

_____?

3 did / the movie / who / with / go to / Bruna

_____?

4 is / apartment / where / new / Susie's

_____?

5 do / how / to / the station / get / you

_____?

6 do / dinner / you / want / what / for

_____?

7 the milk / in / is / the fridge

_____?

8 play / does / sister / the violin / your

_____?

2 Complete the questions to match the answers. Write one or two words in each space.

1 _____ are you _____?
I'm from Peru.

2 _____ is your English teacher?
Mrs Smith is my English teacher.

3 _____ you _____ Max today?
No, I didn't see Max today.

4 _____ you move to New York?
I moved to New York in 2015.

5 _____ his name?
His name is Luca.

6 _____ Maria a teacher?
Yes, she is.

7 _____ Larry very angry?
No, Larry wasn't very angry.

8 _____ you travel to Lima?
We travelled to Lima by plane.

VOCABULARY: Life stages

3 Read about Kazuo's life. Order the phrases. Write 1–6.

a engaged to Eriko _____

b children (two boys) _____

c retired 1990 _____

d born Kyoto, 1930 _____

e married Eriko _____

f primary and secondary school, Tokyo _____

4 Complete the text about Kazuo's life. Write one word in each space.

KAZUO

Kazuo **1**_____ born in Kyoto, in Japan, in 1930. His family moved when he was still a baby and he grew **2**_____ in Tokyo, where he **3**_____ to primary and secondary school. After Kazuo **4**_____ school, he **5**_____ to university to study medicine. At university, he met a girl called Eriko. They **6**_____ engaged, but they waited until after university before they **7**_____ married. They **8**_____ two children. Kazuo worked as a doctor for 30 years. In 1990, after a successful career, he **9**_____ and spent the next twenty years doing what he loved – painting. Sadly, Kazuo **10**_____ in 2015, aged 85.

PRONUNCIATION: Question intonation

5 ▶2.2 Listen to the questions. Does the intonation go up (U) or down (D) at the end?

1 How do you spell your name? _____

2 Do you like cheese? _____

3 Is their house very big? _____

4 When is her birthday? _____

5 Where do you live? _____

6 Did you see Peter? _____

7 Was Anna very angry? _____

8 Who did you go on holiday with? _____

SPEAKING: Telling a personal story

1 ▶ **2.3** Listen to Emma tell Dominic a personal story. Tick (✓) the phrases you hear.

a What happened? _____
b Did I ever tell you about the time …? _____
c That's amazing! _____
d Really? _____
e What did you do then? _____
f Oh no! _____
g You're joking! _____
h That's awful! _____
i That reminds me of … _____
j Lucky you! _____
k Poor you! _____
l You'll never guess … _____
m I felt really … _____

2 ▶ **2.3** Listen again. Which of a–m in exercise 1 do Emma and Dominic use to do these things?

1 Emma tells Dominic something surprising. _____
2 Dominic shows sympathy. _____ _____ _____
3 Emma describes her emotions after the accident happened. _____
4 Dominic shows that he is interested. _____
5 Dominic says that something similar happened to him. _____

3 ▶ **2.4** Listen to six people talking. Choose the best way of showing interest and say it aloud.

1 *Poor you! / What did he do then? / That's amazing!*
2 *What happened? / Oh no! / Lucky you!*
3 *Great! / That's awful! / You're joking!*
4 *What did he do then? / Poor you! / Great!*
5 *What happened? / Lucky you! / Oh no!*
6 *That's amazing! / That's awful! / What happened?*

4 ▶ **2.5** Listen and check your answers to exercise 3.

5 ▶ **2.6** Match the sentence halves. Say them aloud. Then listen and check.

1 Something similar _____
2 That reminds _____
3 You'll never guess _____
4 Let me _____
5 Can you _____
6 I felt _____
7 Did I ever tell _____
8 It was _____

a really nervous about meeting her.
b tell you about my flight to Tokyo.
c you about the time I met Zac Efron?
d so amazing to discover we have the same name!
e imagine how scared I was?
f happened to me when I was a student.
g what happened to Raffie yesterday.
h me of the time I lost my passport.

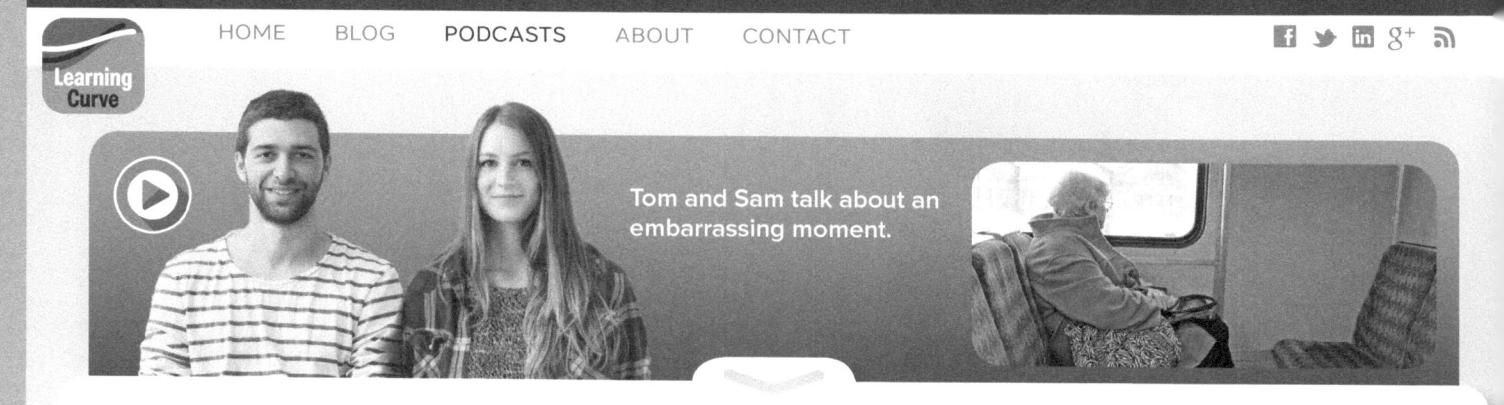

HOME   BLOG   PODCASTS   ABOUT   CONTACT

Learning Curve

Tom and Sam talk about an embarrassing moment.

LISTENING

1 ▶ **2.7** Listen to the podcast. Choose the best summary.

a Maria made friends with an old lady.
b Maria dropped someone's bag on the train.
c Maria upset a complete stranger.

2 ▶ **2.7** Listen again. Choose the correct options to complete the sentences.

1 Maria was surprised by
  a how old the lady was.
  b how smart the lady looked.
  c how interesting the lady was.

2 Maria and the lady had
  a nothing to talk about.
  b little to talk about.
  c a lot to talk about.

3 When she stood up, the lady appeared
  a shorter.
  b younger.
  c older.

4 Maria tried to help the lady by
  a supporting her with her arm.
  b supporting her with her arm and holding her bag.
  c holding her bag.

5 Maria dropped the lady's
  a sweets.
  b bag.
  c stick.

6 The bag fell on
  a the track.
  b the platform.
  c a man.

7 The old lady was
  a very angry.
  b quite calm.
  c too upset to talk.

8 The man helped them by
  a mending the bag.
  b picking up the medicine bottle.
  c getting the bag back.

READING

1 Read the blog about games that use pictures. Complete 1–6 with the adjectives in the box.

annoyed   disappointing   confusing
surprised   interesting   boring

2 Are the sentences true (T), false (F) or is there not enough information to decide (N)?

1 The writer's family play games together every Christmas. _____

2 The writer's sister got more correct answers than their father. _____

3 The writer's mother couldn't name any of the famous people. _____

4 The Spot the Ball competition started in the 1970s. _____

5 The writer's mother played Spot the Ball more than once. _____

6 The writer's father was angry when his wife won a prize. _____

7 The writer's parents didn't earn much money. _____

8 Spot the Ball is less popular today than in the past. _____

9 Spot the Ball is a more difficult competition today than in the 1970s. _____

10 The writer prefers games that use pictures of animals. _____

MONDAY
March 11   **SPOT THE BALL**   № 34747/53

HOME   BLOG   PODCASTS   ABOUT   CONTACT

Tom writes about his favourite games.

Games that use pictures

I'm an amateur photographer, so it's probably not surprising that I love games which are based around images. Last Christmas I organized a quiz for my family. I selected images of different people in the news that year and everyone got one point for each person they could name correctly. My sister thought it was [1]_____, so she didn't really try. I was quite [2]_____ when my dad won – he even managed to recognize Taylor Swift!

Then my parents told me about a game that was very popular in the 1970s called 'Spot the Ball'. It was a simple game in lots of newspapers. You looked at an action shot of a football match, but the ball was removed from the photo and you had to say where you thought it should be. Apparently, my dad found it really [3]_____ and played it every week, but Mum got quite [4]_____ with him, because he wanted to discuss exactly where all the players were looking. Mum used to guess – and one week she won! She only got £100, but that was a lot of money in those days.

Later, I read an article about the game and I was amazed that the last time anyone won the jackpot prize was 2004! About three million people used to play it every week in the 1970s but now there are only about 14,000 players. I think that's a bit [5]_____, because it's great fun.

There's another game that I really enjoy which uses images – you see a very small part of something in detail and you have to work out what it is. There are whole blogs for these kinds of pictures; one of my favourites is http://floorsix.blogspot.co.uk/ . Some of the images are really [6]_____, but to me, that's what makes them even more interesting. I love asking myself questions about them: 'What does it look like?', 'Is it an animal?', 'Is that part of a machine?', 'How big is it really?'. Do you want to have a go at guessing? Look at these three images and try to work out what they are.

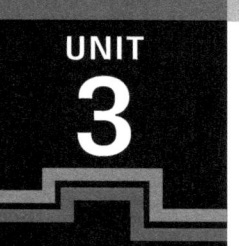

UNIT 3

Keep on travelling

3A | **LANGUAGE**

GRAMMAR: Comparatives, superlatives, *(not) as ... as*

1 Choose the correct options to complete the sentences.

1 The weather here is hotter _____ it is in Germany.
   a most   b than   c as

2 My sister isn't _____ tall as me.
   a as   b than   c more

3 This sofa is _____ comfortable than the other one.
   a most   b as   c more

4 Yusuf is the _____ boy in our class!
   a funniest   b more funny   c funnier

5 For me, Science is _____ lesson of all!
   a the most bad b worst   c the worst

6 Is your house _____ Rafael's?
   a as big than   b as big as
   c more big than

7 Osman makes _____ best cakes in the world!
   a most   b the   c as

8 This is the _____ expensive restaurant in the city.
   a most   b as   c more

2 Complete the conversation with comparative and superlative forms of the adjectives in the box.

> far   cheap   early   important   lazy
> close   crowded   interesting

A Hi Daniel. I heard you moved to a new apartment.

B Yes, I moved to the city centre because I wanted to be ¹_____ to work. Catching the train was so expensive. I can walk everywhere now, which is a lot ²_____.

A I know! I live even ³_____ away than you did. It costs so much, and I think I get ⁴_____ train in the country – it's always completely full in the morning.

B Perhaps you should move as well! I find living in the city a lot ⁵_____ than living in the countryside, too – there's so much to do here.

A I could never live in the city. My horses are the ⁶_____ things in my life. I couldn't live without them!

B Perhaps you should try getting an ⁷_____ train?

A Probably, but I hate getting up in the morning. I'm ⁸_____ person in my family!

VOCABULARY: Useful adjectives

3 Order the letters to make adjectives.

1 I didn't sleep well because the hotel bed was so F R O N T B A U M C E L O.   _____

2 I need to pack my suitcase again because it's too S Y S E M.   _____

3 I didn't think the beach would be so T I Q U E at the weekend.   _____

4 Athens is very N I C E T A N. People have lived there for over 7,000 years.   _____

5 The Eiffel Tower is the most S O M A F U building in Paris.   _____

6 His shop sells L U N U S U A souvenirs that you won't find anywhere else.   _____

4 Complete the text about Tokyo. Some letters are given.

> With nearly 40 million people living there, Tokyo is one of the most ¹ c ___ ___ ___ ___ ___ ___ cities in the world. And it has more cars than anywhere else in Japan, almost 70 million of them, so it's extremely ² p ___ ___ ___ ___ ___ ___ ___ as well. But Tokyo is also one of the top places for foreign tourists to visit. It's very safe and, although it's extremely ³ b ___ ___ ___, many people love the fact that it's really ⁴ l ___ ___ ___ ___ and that there's plenty to see and do. Some visitors may think that ⁵ m ___ ___ ___ ___ ___ buildings like the Sugamo-Shinkin bank, built in 2011, are ⁶ u ___ ___ ___, but others find them quite beautiful and love the fact that they use some of the best 21st century technology.

PRONUNCIATION: Sentence stress

5 ▶ 3.1 Circle the underlined word which is most stressed. Listen, check and repeat.

1 Ali is the <u>best</u> student in <u>his</u> class.

2 My <u>soup</u> doesn't taste as <u>good</u> as Yasmin's.

3 Tokyo is <u>nearer</u> to Mumbai <u>than</u> São Paulo.

4 Is <u>Lady</u> Gaga more <u>famous</u> than Taylor Swift?

5 <u>My</u> car is the most <u>expensive</u> thing I own.

6 Sophia's essay <u>was</u> a lot <u>better</u> than Helena's.

7 It's <u>quieter</u> in the countryside than <u>in</u> the city.

8 I'm feeling <u>a</u> little <u>happier</u> than I was before.

LISTENING: Identifying key points

1 ▶ **3.2** Listen to Joe and Sara talking about holidays. Are the sentences true (T) or false (F)?

1 Sara visits a lot of cities. _____
2 Joe and Sara don't enjoy the same types of holiday. _____
3 Sara doesn't like travelling alone. _____

2 ▶ **3.2** Listen again and choose the correct words to complete the sentences.

1 Sara really likes *cities / beaches / hotels.*
2 Joe doesn't enjoy *going to the beach / going hiking / going abroad.*
3 Sara doesn't like *museums / sunbathing / churches.*
4 A week before Sara leaves, she *books a room / packs her suitcase / buys her plane ticket.*
5 The night before Sara leaves, she *plans her sightseeing / eats out / packs a suitcase.*
6 Sara spends most of her holiday *alone / with other people / on guided tours.*
7 Sara likes travelling alone because she can *choose what to do / read more / go sightseeing.*
8 Sara takes a book when she *goes sightseeing / eats out alone / goes on guided tours.*

3 ▶ **3.3** Underline the key words that are most likely to be stressed by the speaker in these sentences. Listen and check.

1 The museums are crowded in summer.
2 Did you book a seat?
3 We could hire a car at the airport.
4 I'd love to go abroad.
5 The barbecue at the hotel was fantastic.
6 They stay in a beautiful house by the sea.

4 Complete the sentences with the correct form of the verbs in the box.

book	buy	eat out	go
have	hire	visit	stay

1 We both love to _____ in the local restaurants.
2 Could you _____ a double room for my parents, please?
3 Let's _____ a car to drive around the island.
4 My little sister likes to _____ a few souvenirs to take home.
5 My aunt and uncle usually _____ camping in the summer.
6 Lucy and James are _____ in a seaside resort.
7 Today we _____ the local attractions.
8 Peter always _____ a barbecue when he's on holiday.

GRAMMAR: Past continuous and past simple

1 Order the words to make sentences. Add commas where necessary.

1 Alba was / café when / waiting / I arrived / in the

_____.

2 working when / Nehir / was / I / her / left

_____.

3 having / called / Sara / when Lara / a shower / was

_____.

4 he was / Elif lived / at home while / studying / law

_____.

5 I looked / was smiling / that he / at Dad / and saw

_____.

6 still waiting / were / to get in / when the show / started we

_____.

7 her homework / book while / Marian was / I read a / finishing

_____.

8 into the / we were / house while / the thieves / got / sleeping

_____.

9 watching TV / cooking while / were / Mum was / the kids

_____.

10 shopping her friend / while Paola was / went to / the museum

_____.

2 Complete each sentence with the verbs in brackets. Write one past continuous and one past simple form.

1 When we _____ Carlos, he _____ his car. (see, clean)

2 Marta _____ for the train when she _____. (run, fall)

3 Anna _____ Julia while she _____ to class. (meet, walk)

4 Hugo _____ his leg when he _____ tennis. (hurt, play)

5 My phone _____ while I _____. (ring, drive)

6 While Rick _____ his hair, he _____ shampoo in his eyes. (wash, get)

7 Emma _____ late for her lesson because she _____ with Luiza. (be, chat)

8 The plane _____ above the sea when the storm _____. (fly, start)

9 My sister _____ my phone while I _____. (take, not look)

10 When Yasmin _____ her shopping, someo _____ her bag. (do, steal)

PRONUNCIATION: was/were

3 ▶ **3.4** Practise saying the sentences. Pay att to the pronunciation of *was* /wəz/ and *were* / Listen, check and repeat.

1 What were you doing at five o'clock yester

2 I was expecting Monica to call.

3 Rafael was talking to his friend.

4 We were playing outside, but it started *

5 Adam was watching TV while I worked

6 While you were sleeping, I made a ca'

7 I was doing my homework all morni

8 Clara was running when the accide

WRITING: Writing a narrative

1 Read two paragraphs from different parts of a story about a holiday disaster. Choose the correct verbs.

> **A** They went up to the check-in desk, where a woman ¹*checked / was checking* everyone's tickets and passports. Simon ²*gave / was giving* her their passports. The woman took them, then looked at Simon strangely. 'Why did you give me this?' she asked. Then Simon and Gabrielle ³*got / were getting* a terrible shock. They didn't have Gabrielle's passport. They had Simon's passport and Simon's old passport!

> **B** Simon and Gabrielle sat in the car. They felt happy and were chatting. Simon's brother, Toby, ⁴*drove / was driving* them to the airport for their skiing trip. They had to be there by 5.30 a.m. and there weren't any trains that early. They were tired but excited. They had a good journey and Toby ⁵*left / was leaving* them outside the airport. They thanked him and ⁶*went / were going* to get their flight.

2 Read two more paragraphs from different parts of the story. Choose the correct adjectives or adverbs.

> **C** However, when she got back, the airline staff were very ¹*helpful / helpfully*. They ²*kind / kindly* found her a seat on a later flight and she didn't have to pay extra. When she arrived in Switzerland, the coach to the ski resort had gone, but it was easy to catch a bus there. She arrived in time for a ³*delicious / deliciously* dinner, and she quickly forgave Simon. After all, anyone can make a mistake and everything was fine in the end!

> **D** The woman told them rather ⁴*rude / rudely* that Gabrielle couldn't travel. She said that Simon should get on the plane. 'But he's the one who made the mistake!' said Gabrielle. She was really angry. However, there was nothing they could do. Gabrielle had to hire a car and drive back home for her passport. It was a fast journey, but she still missed the plane. She felt very worried and ⁵*miserable / miserably*.

3 Look at these sentences from the text. Rewrite them using adverbs instead of adjectives.

1 They felt happy and were chatting.

They chatted _____.

2 They had a good journey.

The journey went _____.

3 'But he's the one who made the mistake!' said Gabrielle. She was really angry.

'But he's the one who made the mistake!' said Gabrielle _____.

4 It was a fast journey, but she still missed the plane.

She drove _____, but she still missed the plane.

4 Match 1–4 with paragraphs A–D.

1 The background (who, when, where) _____

2 A problem (what happened) _____

3 A resolution (how she solved the problem) _____

4 The ending (what happened in the end, how she felt) _____

5 Write a different last paragraph for the story.

- Use the ideas below or your own ideas.
- Write at least five sentences.
- Use the past continuous and the past simple correctly.
- Use adjectives and adverbs to make your paragraph more interesting.

> **no plane until next day**

> **went to wrong ski resort**

> **Simon was waiting for her at the airport in Switzerland**

> decided to stay at home and not go skiing

> **had a big argument with Simon**

> had to pay for a new ticket

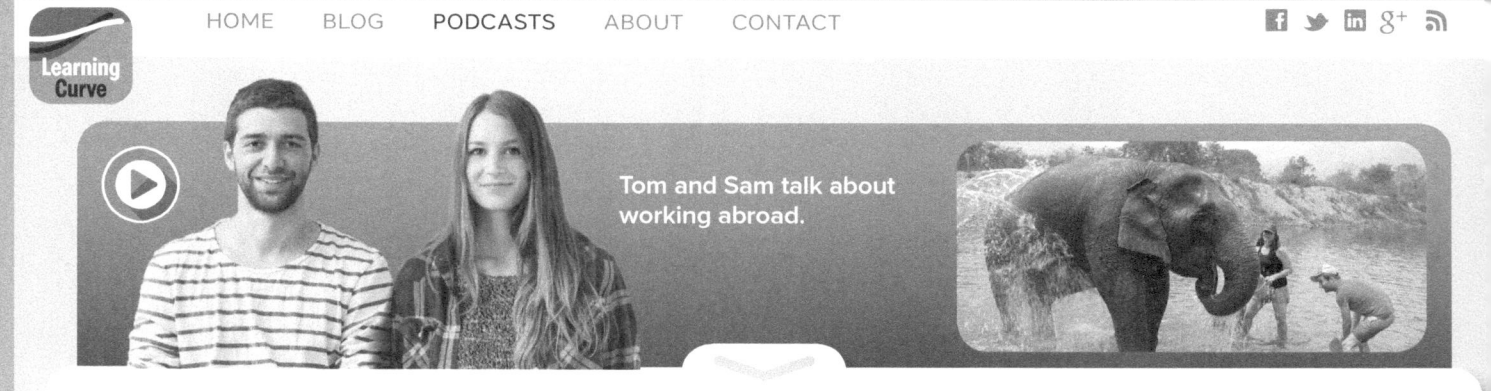

HOME BLOG **PODCASTS** ABOUT CONTACT

Learning Curve

Tom and Sam talk about working abroad.

LISTENING

1 ▶ 3.5 Listen to the podcast. Circle True or False.

1 Mara worked with elephants in Thailand.   True   False

2 She found the work quite easy.   True   False

3 The local people weren't very friendly.   True   False

4 Mara went to Thailand on her own.   True   False

5 One of the animals became ill.   True   False

2 ▶ 3.5 Listen again. Complete the sentences with a maximum of three words.

1 Mara says it was _____ to be so close to the animals.

2 Mara enjoyed being part of a _____.

3 The _____ made the work difficult for Mara.

4 Mara really enjoyed eating the _____.

5 Some of the people Mara worked with went to Thailand in a _____.

6 Mara made _____ with people from around the world.

7 Mara says it's important to _____ a lot there because of the heat.

8 Mara felt better after someone gave her a large _____.

READING

1 Read the blog about four hotels. What do you think the word 'quirkiest' in the heading means?

a most expensive

b most comfortable

c most unusual

d most famous

2 Match the descriptions to hotels A–D.

1 It is a very unusual shape.   _____

2 It is difficult to get into.   _____

3 It has no walls or roof.   _____

4 It is made of a substance not normally used for buildings.   _____

3 Choose the correct options to complete the sentences.

1 The Palacio de Sal is in an area
   a where salt is produced.
   b where many tourists want to go.
   c without normal building materials.

2 According to the blog, the restaurant at the Palacio de Sal
   a makes the best food in Bolivia.
   b makes food that is too salty.
   c makes a popular dish with salt.

3 Jules' Undersea Lodge is
   a in deep water.
   b only reached by taxi.
   c in shallow water.

4 People with heart problems can't stay at Jules' Undersea Lodge because
   a doctors can't reach the hotel.
   b it's not comfortable enough.
   c it is not safe for them.

5 In Dog Bark Park Inn, the beds are
   a in rooms in the dog.
   b shaped like dogs.
   c all in one big room.

6 At Dog Bark Park Inn, real dogs
   a must always be kept inside.
   b are allowed to stay.
   c are not welcome.

7 According to the blog, it is good to stay in a treehouse because
   a you can stay outside all night.
   b you can see unusual animals.
   c it is cheaper than a hotel.

8 According to the blog, sleeping outside means that you can experience
   a being with other people.
   b other aspects of nature.
   c waking up very early.

HOME   BLOG   PODCASTS   ABOUT   CONTACT

Guest blogger Simon writes about hotels.

The world's best places to stay

Four of the world's quirkiest hotels

What do you want from a hotel? Something clean and comfortable for sure, but do you sometimes find your hotel room a little dull? Do you want your nights to be as much a part of your holiday adventure as your days? Here are four recommendations for a stay you'll never forget!

A Palacio de Sal

Most of us know about the ice hotels in countries like Sweden, where everything – even your bed – is made from ice. But this hotel in Bolivia is even more unusual – it is made from salt! 350 km south of the city of La Paz, this hotel is on the edge of the Salar de Uyuni, the world's largest salt plain, and was built using around a million blocks of salt. Visitors report that the food in the restaurant is excellent – especially their famous 'salt chicken'. There's even a swimming pool – filled with salt water, of course!

B Jules' Undersea Lodge

Usually you can get a taxi to your hotel, but not here! To stay in this hotel in Key Largo, you need to scuba dive to reach the entrance. Once you're there, you can watch fish through the windows of your room. Amazingly, there are hot showers, and you can even get pizza delivered! Because you have to dive to get to the lodge, you need to be quite fit. If you have heart problems, or are pregnant, this isn't the place for you!

C Dog Bark Park Inn

This has to be one of the strangest-looking hotels in the world. Owned by a husband and wife team in Idaho, USA, the entire hotel looks like a large wooden dog! Four people can sleep inside the dog – there is even a room in its head. Rooms are filled with doggy decorations, and pets are of course welcome to stay with you!

D Chalkley's Treehouse

A safari is all about being outdoors, right? All about the animals and the wide open spaces. So why go into a building or a tent at night when you could stay under the stars in this treehouse on the Lion Sands Game Reserve in South Africa? You can lie in bed and look up at the stars, watch the sun come up in the morning, and listen to the sound of animals and birds all around you. What could be more romantic?

The working world

4A — LANGUAGE

GRAMMAR: *will*, *may* and *might* for predictions

1 Read the statements. How likely is it that these things will happen? Write 1–8 in the correct columns.

1 Atletico will win the Champions League.
2 She might lose the tennis match.
3 I don't think I will ever travel into space.
4 We might not finish the project on time.
5 They won't complete the work by Friday.
6 We may be able to go camping.
7 Of course, I may not get the job.
8 He'll get there before lunchtime.

Probably (More than 75%)	Possibly (50–75%)	Possibly not (25–50%)	Probably not (Less than 25%)
___	___	___	___
___	___	___	___

2 Complete the sentences with *will*, *won't*, *might*, *think* or *don't think*.

1 I know for sure that Fatma _____ come to the barbecue – she promised she would.
2 Gabriel _____ be home by six o'clock – it depends how much work he has to do.
3 I _____ that Berat will come to the cinema. He's too busy.
4 He definitely _____ come with us on Tuesday. He only goes out at the weekend.
5 I _____ that Vitor will pass his exam. He's so clever and he's been studying so hard.
6 We _____ go to the park for a picnic, although it depends on the weather.
7 I may visit Fernanda this evening, so I probably _____ come to the concert after all.
8 Don't worry, we _____ definitely get to the restaurant on time!
9 The sky looks fairly blue – I _____ that it'll rain today.
10 Our project is going quite well, so we _____ it'll be a success.

VOCABULARY: Jobs

3 Order the letters to complete the jobs.

1 shop TSSAISNTA _____
2 football OCCAH _____
3 fashion SEDGINRE _____
4 film RIDECROT _____
5 police FOFCIER _____
6 tour UGIED _____
7 security UDARG _____
8 travel TEGAN _____

4 Complete the jobs. Some letters are given.

1 I asked an ac_____ for some advice about my money.
2 Luckily, the f_____s stopped the fire within minutes.
3 We needed a l_____ to help us understand the contract.
4 Are all the fruit and vegetables at the market grown by local f_____?
5 She got her h_____ to cut her hair a lot shorter.
6 He's a well-known j_____ and writes for the national newspapers.
7 My cousin's a fashion m_____; she works for all the big designers.
8 We were given our room keys by the r_____ at the hotel.
9 Tomorrow I'll meet the s_____ who's going to operate on my knee.
10 Could you ask the w_____r to bring us some water with our meal?

PRONUNCIATION: *want/won't*

5 ▶ 4.1 Look at the underlined letters and listen to the sentences. Write 1 if the sound is /ɒ/ and 2 if the sound is /əʊ/. Listen, check and repeat.

1 They use r**o**bots in the factory. ___
2 I really w**a**nt to see that film. ___
3 I d**o**n't like cheese at all. ___
4 Do you kn**o**w where he lives? ___
5 My b**o**ss will be at the party tonight. ___
6 Isaac is looking for a j**o**b. ___
7 Manuela's mother used to be a m**o**del. ___
8 How **o**ld is your sister? ___

READING: Skimming a text

1 Read topic sentences A–E in the article. Match each one with the most likely summary 1–5.

1 Evidence from a piece of research. _____
2 The value of time away from work. _____
3 How to reduce our use of handheld devices. _____
4 How technology affects our behaviour. _____
5 Tips to help you concentrate. _____

How to manage **multitasking**

A   We're all multitaskers now, performing two or more tasks at the same time. Whether it's emailing a colleague while checking our smartphones, or writing an essay while catching up on the latest online celebrity gossip, we're all doing it. But should we? Well, recent research suggests it's time to stop demanding so much of our brain and go back to focusing on one thing at a time.

B   Consider the results of a study of workers at a software company. When they stopped working on a major task to answer an email or message, it took ten minutes to be able to fully concentrate again on the original task. Clearly this is not an efficient way of working. Training ourselves to concentrate isn't easy, but psychologist Maria Sylva has some tips:

C   'Let your mind focus on one thing at a time. Whatever task you're doing, make sure you give it your full attention. Giving 100% to the task in hand will help you to work more quickly and more accurately. To begin with this might be tough, so start with short periods – say ten minutes – and work upwards.

D   'If your smartphone is the main source of distraction, leave it at home. If you really believe that the next message you receive will be more interesting or important than your current activity, ask yourself why you are doing that activity.

E   'Give your brain a rest. You'll achieve more if, several times a day, you walk away from tasks that require concentration. And I mean 'walk away'. Don't just look away from your screen or stare out of the window. Get up and leave your desk. If possible, get some fresh air. Taking a complete break will help your brain to come up with new ideas.'

2 Read the whole article, then choose the best ending for each sentence.

1 Maria Sylva wants us to consider whether
   a technology is a good thing in our lives.
   b we should be doing so many things at once.
   c we should use smartphones.

2 The study that she refers to shows that we lose time when we
   a change the task that we are working on.
   b only use email to communicate at work.
   c do not concentrate properly at work.

3 She claims we make fewer mistakes when we
   a work quickly.
   b work for ten minutes at a time.
   c concentrate fully on a task.

4 She tells us not to take a smartphone with us if
   a the messages we get on it are not interesting.
   b it prevents us from giving attention to what we are doing.
   c we leave the house.

5 She recommends
   a putting off tasks that need us to concentrate.
   b taking regular short periods of rest from work.
   c looking away from our screens occasionally.

3 Complete the text with the correct pronouns and possessive adjectives.

Maria Sylva is a life coach. [1]_____ advises people on how to manage [2]_____ time. Most of [3]_____ work is done within companies where she coaches people at all levels, helping [4]_____ to perform to the best of their ability while [5]_____ are working. Maria thoroughly enjoys her job and finds [6]_____ very satisfying. Her aim is to help [7]_____ to achieve the most that we possibly can in [8]_____ working day.

GRAMMAR: *be going to* and present continuous

1 Choose the correct options to complete the sentences.

1 Pablo *going to study / is going to study / studying* medicine next year.

2 What *do you do / you doing / are you doing* this weekend?

3 I *going to / 'm going to / go to* finish my book tonight.

4 We're *visiting / visit / to visit* my parents at the weekend.

5 I'm *meeting / meet / to meet* Daniel and Julia this evening if you'd like to join us.

6 We *going to / 're going to / 're going* book our tickets tomorrow.

7 I *go to / 'm going to / going to* go running in half an hour.

8 My brother *is going to / is going to be / is being* at the festival.

9 Where *do you stay / are you staying / you stay* in Italy this summer?

10 I *go to / 'm going to / going to* ask Nehir if she wants to come to the theatre.

2 Complete the sentences with the verbs in the box. Use the future form in brackets.

> paint bake speak start see rent

1 I can give Azra that book for you. I _____ her next week. (present continuous)

2 I think I _____ to Livia about the problem. (*be going to*)

3 I've decided I _____ a picture of my grandma's garden for her birthday. (*be going to*)

4 I'll be in Portugal for six months. I _____ an apartment in Lisbon. (present continuous)

5 I _____ a cake for Maria's birthday. (*be going to*)

6 Ismail _____ a new job in July. (present continuous)

VOCABULARY: Phrases about work

3 Match the two parts of the sentences.

1 I want to accept the job, but first we need to agree _____

2 She's so unhappy at work. I think she's going to leave _____

3 The interview went well, so I really hope I get _____

4 Think about the questions they might ask before you have _____

5 The first step in applying for a job is to send in the application _____

6 Hasan is hoping that he's going to get a pay _____

7 Lucas is going to advise me on how to write _____

8 You must be looking forward to starting _____

a her job.
b an interview.
c form.
d a salary.
e a CV.
f a job offer.
g work.
h rise.

4 Complete the text about Lucas's job. Some letters are given.

Lucas started a [1] c_____ in nursing five years ago. In January, he saw an [2] a_____ for a job at the local hospital and decided to [3] a_____ for it. They invited him to an [4] i_____ which went very well. Two weeks later, they made him a job [5] o_____. Before he started work, he had to [6] _____ on a training course to improve his skills. Lucas is obviously great at his job. He has already got a [7] p_____ and he now has more responsibility and a big [8] s_____ – he earns much more than I do!

PRONUNCIATION: *going to* and *want to*

5 ▶ 4.2 Listen to the sentences. Pay attention to the pronunciation of *going to* and *want to*. Listen again and repeat.

1 I'm going to apply for that position.

2 I want to leave this job.

3 I don't want to work in an office.

4 She's going to ask for a pay rise.

5 They're going to offer it to her.

6 He's going to write a CV.

SPEAKING: Telephone language

1 ▶ 4.3 Listen to a telephone conversation between Anne, who runs a disco company, and Ryan, a hotel receptionist. Number the phrases in the order that you hear them.

a Could you ask him to call me back, please? _____

b Hello, ... speaking. _____

c I'm afraid he's not available at the moment. _____

d How can I help you? _____

e Thanks for calling. _____

f Could I speak to ...? _____

g Can I take a message? _____

h Can you tell him that ...? _____

2 Complete the table with a–h from exercise 1.

Caller	Person being called
_____	_____
_____	_____
_____	_____
	_____
	_____

3 ▶ 4.4 Complete the conversation with phrases for dealing with difficulties. Then listen and check.

A Good morning, Hobson's department store, Helen speaking. How can I help you?

B Hello, could I speak to someone in the electrical department, please?

A Sorry, could you [1]_____ up? This line's really bad. [2]_____ speak more slowly, please?

B Yes, I'd like to speak to someone in the electrical department, please.

A Of course. I'll put you through to Simon Jones. He's in charge of electrical goods.

... Oh, I'm sorry. I'm afraid he's not available at the moment. He'll be back at eleven o'clock.

B Sorry, did [3]_____ eleven?

A That's right. Shall I ask him to call you?

B Yes, please. My number is 0755 511817.

A Could you [4]_____, please?

B Yes, it's 0755 511817. Oh, and could you tell him that it needs to be as small as possible because I don't have much shelf space in my bedroom?

A I'm afraid I [5]_____ that.

B Don't worry, I'll tell him when he calls.

A OK. And can I take your name, please?

B Robert Faux.

A Can [6]_____ that, please?

B F-A-U-X.

A [7]_____ A-U or E-U?

B A-U.

A Great, thank you. Simon will call you later. Goodbye.

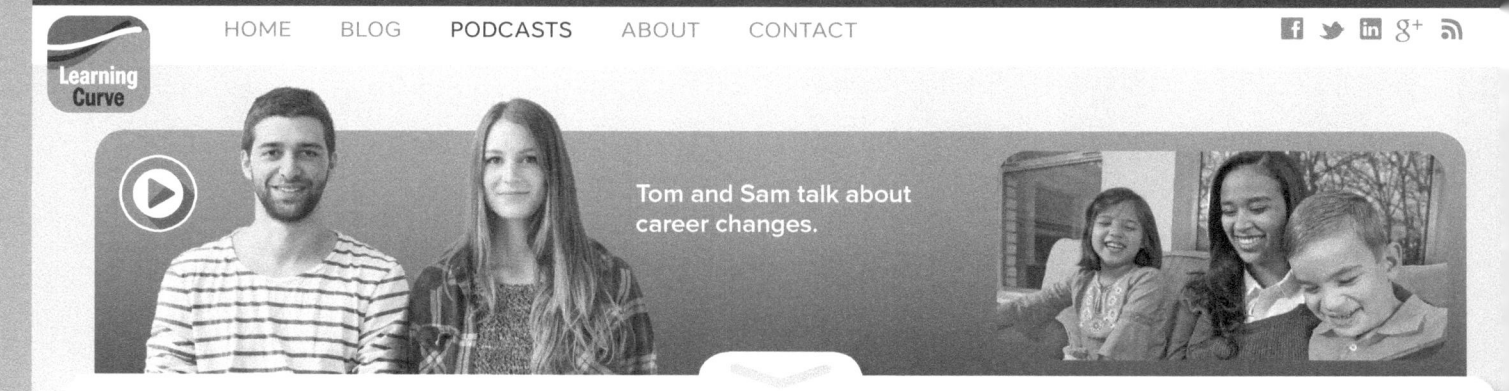

Learning Curve

HOME   BLOG   PODCASTS   ABOUT   CONTACT

Tom and Sam talk about career changes.

LISTENING

1 ▶ **4.5** Listen to the podcast. Choose the correct statement.

  a Larissa had problems at work and was extremely unhappy.

  b Larissa didn't want to do the same thing forever.

  c Larissa hated being an accountant and prefers being a teacher.

2 ▶ **4.5** Listen again. Are the sentences true (T) or false (F)?

  1 Larissa earned a lot of money as an accountant. _____

  2 The people she worked with were much younger than her. _____

  3 She found an interesting job advert in a newspaper. _____

  4 She was very surprised when she got the job. _____

  5 She loved her time on the island. _____

  6 She does not have definite plans for the future. _____

  7 She might work as an accountant again. _____

  8 She's definitely going to use her teaching skills in her next job. _____

READING

1 Read the blog about seven different careers. Match descriptions A–G with these jobs.

  1 accountant _____

  2 fashion designer _____

  3 hairdresser _____

  4 journalist _____

  5 lawyer _____

  6 receptionist _____

  7 sales person _____

2 Match each person with the job (A–G) that would be most suitable.

  1 Evie is a patient and hardworking person. She enjoys talking to people and she always dresses well – her appearance is really important to her! _____

  2 Jamie has a great imagination. He has always been good at Art and is quite good at Maths. He's not at all shy and is confident about learning new skills. _____

  3 Hannah loves everything to do with fashion. She knows what makes people look great – and what doesn't – and isn't afraid to tell them! She enjoys learning, too. _____

  4 Marcus is very sociable; he's good at talking and gets on well with all sorts of people. He's also very honest and can usually tell if someone is lying. _____

  5 Raj has excellent speaking and writing skills. He always did well at school and is keen to study hard at university. He hates making mistakes! _____

HOME   BLOG   PODCASTS   ABOUT   CONTACT

Guest blogger Marc writes about seven interesting careers.

Find the right career for you

A To be successful, you must be passionate about the truth. You'll need the confidence to ask people difficult questions. You may need to make yourself unpopular with important people. And of course, you'll need excellent written skills, as well as being able to communicate clearly.

B This is a very creative job, so you need strong drawing skills. However, you should be able to see your clothes in your head *before* you put your pencil to paper. But loving clothes and being good at art isn't enough – it's a competitive business and you need to understand your markets and be able to calculate the cost of materials, etc.

C This will only suit you if you're someone who pays attention to detail – your work must be completely accurate. You also need good time-management skills: financial information is extremely important for a business and must be available at the right time. Many top people in this job are senior managers, so if you do well, you might get promoted quickly.

D You're often the first person a customer meets when they visit a company or a hotel, so you must look smart and communicate in a friendly professional way. You might have to deal with difficult or rude people, so you need to be calm and polite. You don't need lots of qualifications, but you will need to use your firm's computer and phone systems.

E If you think you'll be good at this, don't do it! You need to be *great*, not good! The best people are extremely confident and excellent communicators, but that doesn't mean talking all the time – you need to listen, too. Above all, you need to know when it's worth pushing, and when to walk away.

F For such a competitive career, you'll need excellent exam results to do a degree course. You'll need to analyse information quickly and accurately, and using language effectively is essential, for understanding technical documents and communicating with clients. And you must be able to express yourself clearly and logically.

G This is a creative job – up to a point! Relationships are important, too, and you can earn respect by giving clients good advice – there's no point giving a perfect cut if it doesn't suit someone's face and features. You don't have to do particularly well at school, but you need strong technical skills – the best professionals do courses all through their career.

Mind and body

5A — **LANGUAGE**

GRAMMAR: *should/shouldn't*

1 Match problems 1–8 with the best advice and circle *should* or *shouldn't* in a–h.

1 My car keeps breaking down. _____
2 I feel so tired all the time. _____
3 I'm extremely stressed at work. _____
4 I never have enough money to go on holiday. _____
5 I have a lot of problems with my teeth. _____
6 I'm bored of going to the same club. _____
7 I sometimes get quite lonely. _____
8 I never get good grades for my homework. _____

a You *should / shouldn't* spend so much on clothes.
b You *should / shouldn't* ask your teacher's advice.
c You *should / shouldn't* stay up late.
d You *should / shouldn't* try the one that's just opened.
e You *should / shouldn't* make some new friends.
f You *should / shouldn't* buy a better one.
g You *should / shouldn't* eat sweets every day.
h You *should / shouldn't* speak to your boss.

2 Complete the sentences with *should* or *shouldn't* and the verbs in the box.

pay let feel give up ask
visit apologize do

1 I couldn't believe how rude Paul was – you _____ him speak to you like that!
2 I can't afford to pay my rent. What do you think I _____?
3 We didn't do anything wrong, so we _____ guilty.
4 It wasn't your fault, so I don't think you _____.
5 Boris broke the chair, so I think he _____ for a new one.
6 Your piano lessons are going well – you definitely _____!
7 My friend Beatriz is in hospital. I _____ her later.
8 Do you think Ryan _____ Helen to go out with him?

VOCABULARY: Health and medicine

3 Choose the correct options to complete the sentences.

1 He had to carry a heavy box and now he has _____.
   a flu   b backache   c a sore throat
2 I can't play tennis for weeks because my arm is _____.
   a stressed   b sore   c broken
3 Feel Mila's face to see if she has _____.
   a a temperature   b a cold   c earache.
4 I have a painful _____ so I can only eat soup!
   a headache   b earache   c sore throat
5 Felipe has a bad _____ – we could hear it in the night.
   a headache   b cough   c toothache
6 Charlie is _____ because he has too much work to do.
   a stressed   b sore   c broken

4 Complete the words.

1 I touched the hot oven and b_____ my hand.
2 I have t_____ so I'm going to see the dentist.
3 Don't play with that knife, Enzo, or you'll c_____ yourself!
4 Davi's daughter ate too much ice cream and got stomach a_____.
5 The ball hit Luiza in the face and gave her a nose b_____.
6 He h_____ his leg badly and couldn't walk for days.

PRONUNCIATION: *should/shouldn't*

5 ▶ 5.1 Listen to the sentences and write *should* or *shouldn't*. Listen, check and repeat.

1 Do you think I _____ tell Rob the news?
2 Gloria _____ spend so much money on clothes.
3 You _____ chat during lessons.
4 I agree that David _____ get a new job.
5 Perhaps Maria _____ spend more time studying.
6 You really _____ eat so much before you exercise!
7 I don't believe you _____ worry about that.
8 He _____ have less sugar in his coffee.

LISTENING: Listening in detail

1 ▶ **5.2** Listen to Rebecca making a phone call to Joey. Are the sentences true (T) or false (F)?

1 Joey is Rebecca's brother. _____
2 Joey is at work. _____
3 Joey wasn't feeling well in June. _____
4 Rebecca tells Joey to see a doctor. _____
5 Joey doesn't have a job at the moment. _____
6 Rebecca wants to see Joey. _____

2 ▶ **5.2** Listen again. Choose the best options to complete the sentences.

1 Rebecca thinks Joey is
   a at the doctor's.
   b in bed.
   c with his mother.

2 Rebecca's mother said that Joey had
   a a cough.
   b a sore throat.
   c a cough and a sore throat.

3 In London, Rebecca tried to persuade Joey to
   a see a doctor.
   b get a different job.
   c work fewer hours.

4 Rebecca has a
   a cold.
   b cough.
   c sore throat.

5 Rebecca talks about
   a visiting Joey.
   b cooking a meal for Joey.
   c taking Joey to the doctor's.

3 ▶ **5.3** Read these sentences from Rebecca's phone call. Mark the links between consonants and vowels. Listen again and check.

1 I'm just calling for a chat.
2 ... you're not feeling so well again.
3 She said you have a bad cough and a sore throat.
4 I'm just a bit worried about your health.
5 You seemed a bit stressed about work when we met in London.
6 I don't think that job is good for you.

4 Choose the correct verb collocations.

1 When do you usually *make / do / take* your homework?
2 *Make / Have / Take* a deep breath and try to relax.
3 If you *make / do / have* a mistake, put a line through it.
4 When we *make / have / do* an argument, Sophie always wins!
5 It's a difficult exam, so just *make / do / take* your best.
6 We must *make / do / have* a decision about where to go on holiday.
7 If you're tired, why don't you *take / have / do* a little rest?
8 Let's *make / take / have* a chat over a cup of coffee.

GRAMMAR: First conditional

1 Order the words to make first conditional sentences. Add commas where necessary.

1 the party / if / have / rains we'll / inside / it

_____.

2 miss / the / you don't / hurry / train if / you'll

_____.

3 Luiz I / can give / if I / the message / him / see

_____.

4 have / problems just / if you / any / call me

_____.

5 the cinema / tired I / if / might not / I'm / come to

_____.

6 be disappointed / if he / get the / there / job he'll / doesn't

_____.

7 I have / from / phone you / the airport if / enough time / I'll

_____.

8 if Ezgi / her I'll / be home / soon / I'll / calls tell

_____.

2 Complete the first conditional sentences with the verbs in brackets in the correct form.

1 If Mirac _____ (agree), we _____ (go) on the train.

2 We _____ (not have) a picnic if the weather _____ (not be) good.

3 Mum _____ (be) cross if we _____ (get) home late.

4 If you _____ (not take) any medicine, you _____ (not feel) better.

5 If the machine _____ (stop), _____ (press) this button.

6 I _____ (call) you if I _____ (need) a lift home.

7 Leonardo _____ (be) upset if we _____ (forget) his birthday.

8 You _____ (hurt) yourself if you _____ (not be) careful!

VOCABULARY: Emotions and feelings

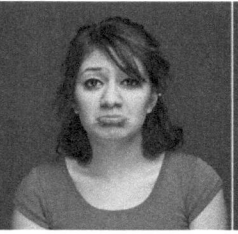

3 Match definitions 1–6 with adjectives a–f.

1 feeling worried about something _____

2 unhappy or sad _____

3 extremely happy about something _____

4 not worried or anxious _____

5 sad because you're alone _____

6 sure of your own abilities _____

   a delighted

   b confident

   c calm

   d nervous

   e upset

   f lonely

4 Complete the adjectives.

1 Her husband was very j_____ and didn't like her speaking to other men.

2 Vitor was p_____ of his new trainers and showed them to all his friends.

3 You're very c_____ this morning! What's making you smile so much?

4 When I realized how badly I'd upset her, I felt g_____.

5 She was crying all the time and was extremely m_____.

6 I'm e_____ of your beautiful coat! I wish I had one.

PRONUNCIATION: 'll contraction

5 ▶ 5.4 Listen to the sentences. Is *will* contracted? Circle the correct answer.

1 contracted / not contracted

2 contracted / not contracted

3 contracted / not contracted

4 contracted / not contracted

5 contracted / not contracted

6 contracted / not contracted

7 contracted / not contracted

WRITING: Writing an informal email

1 Read Izzie's email asking for advice about making friends. Number a–i in the order they appear. The first answer is given.

a asking about the person you are writing to ____

b mentioning a completely different subject ____

c the ending ____

d the reason for writing ____

e the greeting ____

f making an arrangement ____

g the request for a response ____

h the subject of the email ____ *1*

i the details of the problem ____

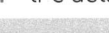

To: annabrown67@quickmail.com

RE: Advice, please!

Hi Bella!

How's it going? Hope you're enjoying your new job! Did I tell you I left home last month? I'm living in an amazing apartment in Antofagasta now.

That's why I'm writing. I'm having a really bad time, and I wanted to ask you for some advice.

My new apartment's big, and it's quite nice, but I'm so lonely! I'm a bit shy (as you know!) so I'm finding it very hard to make new friends. I miss my family so much now that I don't see them very often – especially my mum (I know – I'm such a baby!).

What do you think I should do? How did you make friends when you left home? And when will I stop feeling so bad?!

Anyway, there's some good news, which is that my brother's getting married in June! I'm really looking forward to the wedding.

Do you fancy going out for a pizza next time I'm home, if you aren't too busy? There's a new pizza restaurant – it's a bit expensive, but not too bad. Let me know!

See you later,

Izzie, x

2 Write the contracted forms of these verbs. Which six are in Izzie's email?

1 you are   _____

2 she has   _____

3 I am   _____

4 it is   _____

5 they have   _____

6 there is   _____

7 do not   _____

8 did not   _____

9 are not   _____

3 Complete the sentences with *extremely*, *not very*, *quite* or *bit*. Use each one once.

1 I want to take more exercise but I'm a _____ nervous about going to a gym.

2 It's _____ healthy to eat so much junk food.

3 My friend goes running every day so she's _____ fit.

4 These dance classes are _____ easy – they're suitable for most people.

4 Read the problem below, then write an email to a friend, asking for their advice.

Your doctor says you are quite unhealthy.

You need to get fit and improve your diet, but you don't know how to.

You don't do sport and you love pizza and ice cream.

- Structure the email with a subject, greeting, reason for writing, details, request for response and an ending.
- Use contractions like *I'm* and *don't*.
- Use informal words like *Hi, How's it going?* and *anyway*.
- Use modifiers like *extremely* and *a bit* to make adjectives and adverbs stronger or weaker.

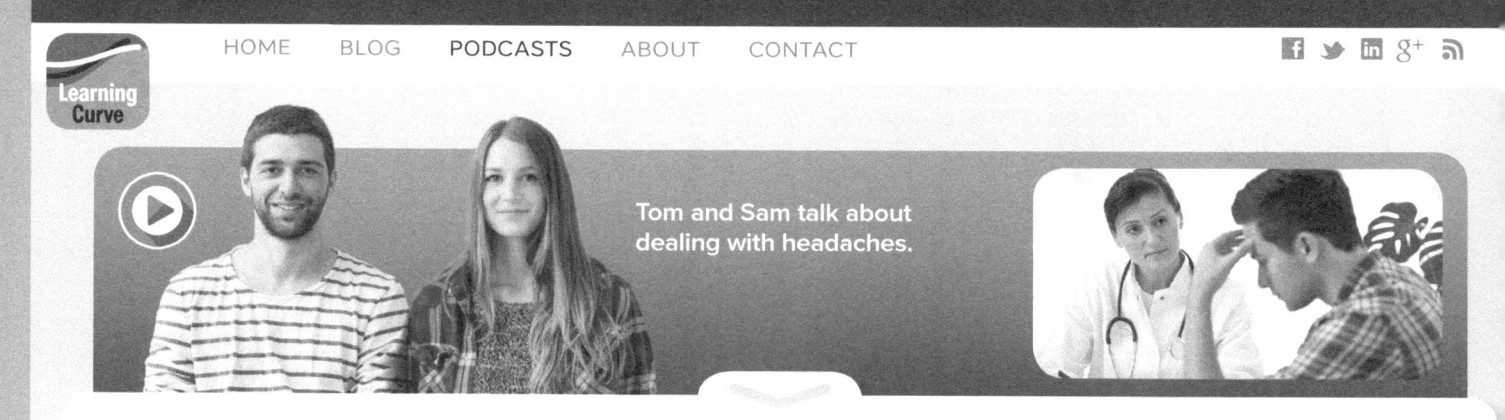

Learning Curve

HOME   BLOG   **PODCASTS**   ABOUT   CONTACT

Tom and Sam talk about dealing with headaches.

LISTENING

1 ▶ **5.5** Listen to the podcast. Does the speaker say these things? Circle Yes or No.

1	Headaches are the most common health problem in the UK.	Yes	No
2	Tension headaches are ones that most people get occasionally.	Yes	No
3	Many headaches are caused by people's lifestyles.	Yes	No
4	Sleeping too much can cause headaches.	Yes	No
5	Yoga may help to prevent headaches.	Yes	No

2 ▶ **5.5** Listen again. Complete the sentences with a maximum of three words.

1 In the UK, more than _____ people have headaches regularly.

2 Bad headaches can make work or _____ life difficult.

3 You should see a doctor if you have other symptoms such as a high _____.

4 Tension headaches last for about _____.

5 You can treat most headaches with _____ from the pharmacy.

6 The doctor advises drinking _____ glasses of water daily.

7 It's a good idea to sleep _____ hours every night.

8 Work or studying can cause _____ which leads to headaches.

READING

1 Read the blog about how to live to be 100. Match headings A–D with paragraphs 1–4.

A A difficult choice _____

B Don't forget to clean your teeth! _____

C Look at the data _____

D Healthy mind, healthy body _____

2 Choose the correct options to complete the sentences.

1 *Most / Few / Hardly any* people born after 2000 will live to 100.

2 From 1900–2000 life expectancy increased *more than / less than / the same amount as* in previous centuries.

3 People born before 2000 *can / can't / are likely to* live to be 100.

4 *All / Some / None* of the men who took part in the Swedish study were slim and active.

5 To live a long life, it's important to *take medicine / have children / enjoy yourself*.

6 If your father lives to 100, you are *more likely / less likely / about as likely* to live to 100 yourself.

7 For a long life, it *is better / is worse / makes no difference* if you have a young mother.

8 A woman who has a child after 44 has *more chance / less chance / about the same chance* of dying young compared to a woman who has children when she's younger.

9 To live to 100, what's best for the child is *the same as / different from / more important than* what's best for the mother.

10 People with poor teeth are likely to die *before / later than / at the same time as* people with healthy teeth.

HOME **BLOG** PODCASTS ABOUT CONTACT

Guest blogger Taylor explains how to live longer.

How to get to 100 ... *and beyond!*

The great news for anyone born after the year 2000 is that they're likely to live to 100. In fact, life expectancy went up by 30 years between 1900 and 2000 – the fastest increase ever! But people born before 2000 shouldn't be too jealous – many scientists say it's possible for them to live longer, too. But health advice seems to change from year to year, so how do we know what we should do if we want to live to 100?

1 Scientists in Sweden followed the lives of 855 men, all born before 1931. Ten of them lived to 100, and they all had certain things in common: they were slim and active, they did exercise, they didn't smoke, and they kept themselves busy and cheerful.

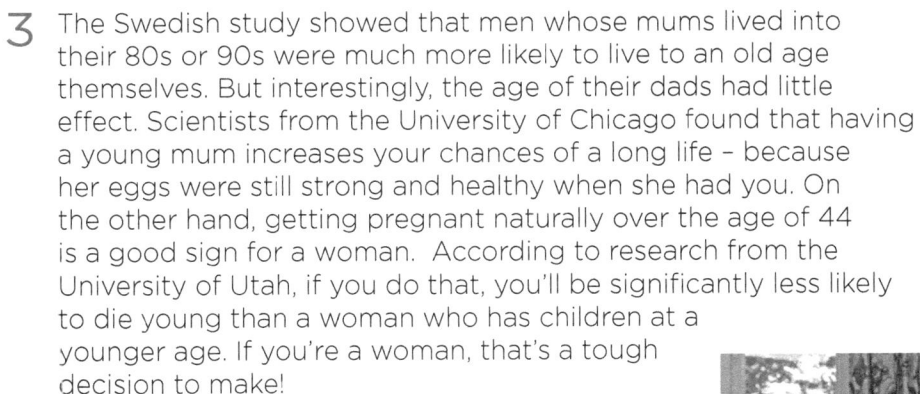

2 It seems that if we want to live a long life, we should make sure we have a good time! Research shows that having interests and a feeling of purpose in life often does more to keep us young than tablets and medicines. And numerous studies have proved how important it is to have a strong circle of friends, so you definitely shouldn't spend too much time on your own.

3 The Swedish study showed that men whose mums lived into their 80s or 90s were much more likely to live to an old age themselves. But interestingly, the age of their dads had little effect. Scientists from the University of Chicago found that having a young mum increases your chances of a long life – because her eggs were still strong and healthy when she had you. On the other hand, getting pregnant naturally over the age of 44 is a good sign for a woman. According to research from the University of Utah, if you do that, you'll be significantly less likely to die young than a woman who has children at a younger age. If you're a woman, that's a tough decision to make!

4 That's what your parents always told you when you were a child, and it turns out to be very good advice! Scientists have discovered that the bacteria that grow in a dirty mouth can cause heart problems, which may even lead to early death. So, strange as it may seem, if you brush carefully, you can prevent heart attacks as well as toothache!

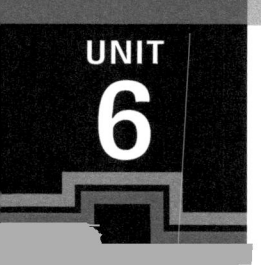

UNIT 6

Risks and experiences

6A — LANGUAGE

GRAMMAR: Present perfect with *ever* and *never*

1 Choose the correct options to complete the conversation.

> **Gabriela** ¹*Have / Did* you ever been skiing, Juliana?
>
> **Juliana** No, I ²*didn't / haven't*, but I'd like to. How about you?
>
> **Gabriela** Yes, I ³*have been / went* once when I was at school. I loved it.
>
> **Juliana** Actually, my brother's ⁴*gone / been* to Italy on a skiing holiday. He's there until Saturday.
>
> **Gabriela** Lucky him! ⁵*Have / Has* he ever been before?
>
> **Juliana** Yes, he's ⁶*gone / been* a few times, although this time he's going with his girlfriend, and she's ⁷*never / ever* tried skiing.

2 Complete the conversations. Write one or two words in each space.

1 **A** _____ you _____ seen a tiger in the wild?

   B Yes, I _____ one in India last year – it was amazing!

2 **A** Have you _____ been to New York?

   B Yes, I _____ there several times.

3 **A** Have you ever tried snowboarding?

   B No, I have _____ done that.

4 **A** _____ Matheus ever _____ to Turkey?

   B Yes, he went there last summer.

5 **A** Has your sister ever been engaged?

   B No, she _____.

VOCABULARY: Phrasal verbs

3 Match the two parts of the sentences.

1 Poor Belinda! Her car broke _____

2 I really want to find _____

3 He wants to get fit and has decided to take _____

4 Could you buy some coffee? We've run _____

5 I'm a bit cold. Could you turn _____

6 I didn't know the word, so I looked it _____

   a out who took my phone.

   b on the heating, please?

   c up in the dictionary.

   d out of it.

   e up cycling in the evenings.

   f down on the way to work.

4 Complete the phrasal verbs.

1 I'll borrow your jacket and **give** it _____ on Saturday.

2 Shall I **carry** _____ with this exercise or finish it later?

3 There should be plenty of petrol as I **filled** _____ the car yesterday.

4 It started as a small project, but **turned** _____ a huge job.

5 Could you help me **tidy** _____ , please?

6 You need to **fill** _____ this application form.

7 I'll be ready in a minute if you just **hold** _____.

8 Felipe has **given** _____ eating meat for environmental reasons.

9 Shall we keep these magazines or **throw** them _____ ?

10 I had to **look** _____ my younger brother while my parents were out.

PRONUNCIATION: Irregular past participles

5 ▶6.1 Practise saying the sentences. Pay attention to the pronunciation of *-en*. Listen, check and repeat.

1 I've never driv**en** in the snow.

2 Have you ever writt**en** a poem?

3 She's never giv**en** a speech before.

4 Has he ever spok**en** to her?

5 I've never forgott**en** my parents' birthdays.

6 We have never eat**en** at that café.

7 Have you chos**en** your dessert yet?

8 Has she tak**en** her driving test?

READING: Guessing the meaning of words from context

VOLCANO BOARDING

COOL OR CRAZY?

The idea of speeding down the side of a volcano, while clinging with all your strength to a little piece of wood, might strike most of us as terrifying. But some people travel thousands of miles to do just this. Every year, huge groups of thrill-seekers travel to western Nicaragua's Cerro Negro mountain to take part in the new extreme sport of volcano boarding.

Participants, dressed head to foot in protective clothing, reach speeds of 80 km per hour on their specially adapted surfboards. They hike up one side of the volcano, have a training session, and then 'surf' down the other, having paused to admire the spectacular view from the top. Some stand as they race down, surfer-style, while others sit. All agree that it's exhilarating, though not everyone who does it is in a hurry to repeat it:

'I've never experienced anything like it!' said Jamie Whyte from London. 'It's completely unique. But though it's great to be able to say I've done it, I'm in no rush to have another go! To steer, you hold onto a rope that's attached to the front of the board and you pull it one way or the other, but I'm not sure I did it properly because I ended up crashing into some rocks. You can slow yourself down by keeping your feet in contact with the ground as you go, but again, I didn't quite get the hang of this, and I reached a really scary speed on the way down!'

1 Read the article about a new sport. Write T for true sentences, F for false sentences, and N when the article doesn't give you enough information to be sure.

1 Nicaragua's Cerro Negro mountain is the only place to do this sport. _____

2 You can use an ordinary surfboard for this activity. _____

3 Volcano boarders have to walk up one side of the mountain. _____

4 Jamie Whyte is keen to take part in this sport again. _____

5 He hurt himself on the way down. _____

6 He was frightened by how fast he moved. _____

2 Find the words in bold in the text, then choose the correct definitions.

1 If someone is **clinging** to something, they are
   a lying on it.
   b sliding off it.
   c holding it tightly.

2 Something that is **terrifying** is extremely
   a frightening.
   b exciting.
   c strange.

3 A **thrill-seeker** is someone who likes
   a doing exciting and dangerous activities.
   b doing a lot of exercise.
   c travelling to new places.

4 A **participant** is someone who
   a has not done something before.
   b trains people to do something.
   c takes part in something.

5 If something is **spectacular**, it is
   a amazing to look at.
   b extremely dangerous.
   c very unusual.

6 An activity that is **exhilarating** makes you feel
   a stressed and worried.
   b happy and excited.
   c relaxed.

7 Something that is **unique** is
   a different from anything else.
   b exactly like something else.
   c very ordinary.

8 To **steer** something is to
   a make it go faster.
   b make it go slower.
   c control its direction.

9 If you **get the hang of** something, you
   a learn how to do it.
   b fail to do it well.
   c start to learn how to do it.

3 Complete the sentences about volcano boarding with the linkers *and, also, as well* and *too*.

1 He found volcano boarding quite frightening and he _____ found it difficult.

2 Participants experience the thrill of speed and get to see fantastic views, _____.

3 The mountain side is very steep _____ it's also extremely long.

4 People taking part wear special suits. They _____ wear helmets.

5 The side of the volcano is hot. It's very hard _____.

6 It's a demanding sport _____ it also requires a degree of training.

GRAMMAR: Second conditional

1 Choose the correct options to complete the sentences.

1 If you could live anywhere in the world, _____?
   a where would you live
   b where do you live
   c where will you live

2 You'd be less tired _____.
   a if you are going to bed earlier
   b if you went to bed earlier
   c if you go to bed earlier

3 If you spoke to Luiz, _____.
   a you can explain the situation
   b you could explain the situation
   c you will be able to explain the situation

4 You would lose weight _____.
   a if you ate less
   b if you were eating less
   c if you eat less

5 If you had more money, _____?
   a what did you buy
   b what would you buy
   c what are you buying

6 If you left now, _____.
   a you could catch the bus
   b you can catch the bus
   c you will be able to catch the bus

7 I would take the job _____.
   a if they offer it to me
   b if they are offering it to me
   c if they offered it to me

2 Complete the second conditional sentences with the verbs in brackets in the correct order.

1 If Manuel _____ to save enough money, he _____ a new motorbike. (buy, manage)

2 If I _____ you, I _____ Hasan for advice. (be, ask)

3 If she _____ more time, she _____ a foreign language. (have, learn)

4 Amanda _____ better grades if she _____ harder. (study, get)

5 If you _____ nearer to me, we _____ each other more. (live, see)

6 If I _____ rich, I _____ my job. (give up, become)

VOCABULARY: The natural world

3 Order the letters to make words that match the definitions.

1 a small river MASTER _____

2 animals and plants in their natural environment LIDWEFIL _____

3 the land along the edge of the sea HERSO _____

4 when it gets light in the morning SIRENUS _____

5 a low area of land, often with a river through it LAYVEL _____

6 a huge area of water, like the Atlantic NOACE _____

4 Complete the words.

1 Those w___ ___ ___ ___ are huge – they'd be great for surfing.

2 There are some fantastic underground c___ ___ ___ ___ that you can explore.

3 The r___ ___ ___ ___ of these trees go several metres deep.

4 There was a fantastic s___ ___ ___ ___ ___ this evening – the sky was pink and orange.

5 I picked some apples from the tree's lower b___ ___ ___ ___ ___ ___ ___.

6 From his room he could see the mountain's snow-covered p___ ___ ___ s.

PRONUNCIATION: Sentence stress

5 ▶ 6.2 <u>Underline</u> the words you think will be stressed. Listen, check and repeat.

1 If I were you, I'd be annoyed.

2 She'd go back to college if she could afford it.

3 If you could play any instrument, what would it be?

4 If she was taller, she could be a model.

5 If Larissa came to the party, Alex would be happy.

6 I'd join you at the restaurant if I could leave work earlier.

7 Fatma would be happier if she had more friends.

8 If I didn't have to work, I'd go to the cinema.

SPEAKING: Agreeing and disagreeing

1 ▶ **6.3** Listen to Antonio and Carrie discussing holiday plans. Are the statements true (T) or false (F)?

1 Carrie likes Antonio's suggestions for what to do on holiday. _____

2 Antonio wants to do lots of different activities. _____

3 Antonio likes places that are popular with tourists. _____

4 They decide not to go on holiday together. _____

2 ▶ **6.3** Listen again. Match phrases 1–8 with Antonio or Carrie's reasons for using them (a–h).

1 Absolutely! _____

2 I don't know. _____

3 Exactly! _____

4 Oh, come on! _____

5 I don't think so. _____

6 I suppose so. _____

7 I'm not sure about that. _____

8 You're right. _____

a Carrie doesn't want fresh air and exercise.

b Antonio admits that they are both tourists.

c Carrie agrees that they should decide on a holiday.

d Antonio agrees with Carrie's suggestion for a holiday.

e Carrie disagrees that being alone would be good.

f Carrie isn't keen on a physically active holiday.

g Antonio prefers not to have wi-fi or comfortable beds.

h Antonio doesn't want to stay in a comfortable hotel.

3 ▶ **6.4** Complete the phrases for taking turns. Listen again and check.

1 I fancy doing something exciting, something that's a physical challenge. What _____?

2 Sorry, Antonio, you _____ ...

3 It would be nice to get away from the rest of the world. _____ think so?

4 Go _____, Carrie.

4 ▶ **6.5** Read the opinions. Then listen and respond using the phrases from exercise 2 and your own reasons.

1 It's best to go on holiday on your own because you're more likely to meet interesting people.

2 Everyone should travel as much as possible. You can't understand the world if you haven't seen it!

3 Sports like sailing and mountain climbing aren't dangerous if you use the right equipment.

4 All students should take a year off from studying to go travelling.

HOME   BLOG   PODCASTS   ABOUT   CONTACT

Learning Curve

Tom and Sam talk about survival courses.

LISTENING

1 ▶ 6.6 Listen to the podcast. Number these things 1–5 in the order the speaker mentions them.

a   how to find drinking water ____
b   working out where you are ____
c   the sort of people who do survival courses ____
d   how to create smoke signals ____
e   how to make a fire ____

2 ▶ 6.6 Listen again. Choose the correct options to complete the sentences.

1   Sofia's course taught people how to
a   become a soldier.
b   survive in the wild.
c   deal with danger in Canada.

2   Sofia did the course because she
a   knew someone whose plane had crashed.
b   wanted to meet people with different jobs.
c   wanted to learn skills for dangerous situations.

3   The most important thing Sofia learned was how to
a   get water to drink.
b   find food in the wild.
c   make a shelter.

4   Sofia doesn't want to hunt animals because
a   it's too difficult.
b   she doesn't eat meat.
c   they frighten her.

5   Sofia learned how to use the sun to
a   walk in a straight line.
b   cross rivers safely.
c   see where she was walking.

6   Sofia learned how to get help by
a   being prepared.
b   waving to people.
c   lighting a fire.

READING

1 Read the blog about travelling alone. Tick (✔) the things the writer talks about.

a   safety advice for women ____
b   the laws in different countries ____
c   choosing the best restaurants ____
d   finding the cheapest flights ____
e   organizing accommodation ____
f   meeting the local people ____

2 Are the statements true (T) or false (F), according to the blog?

1   Other travellers can often give you useful tips. ____
2   The writer had an enjoyable holiday travelling around Turkey. ____
3   When travelling with friends, you sometimes have to do things you don't enjoy. ____
4   It's good to be able to change your mind about what you want to do on holiday. ____
5   Women are always in more danger than men when travelling alone. ____
6   Drinks are usually more expensive in other countries. ____
7   It's better to find out about a country when you arrive, not before. ____
8   People who try travelling alone may find they prefer it. ____

HOME   BLOG   PODCASTS   ABOUT   CONTACT

Guest blogger Ethan gives some tips on travelling on your own.

Holidaying alone

Have you ever taken a holiday alone? For many people, it's a terrifying thought. They worry about being lonely, that accommodation will cost more, and that it might be dangerous. But it doesn't have to be that way!

If you go with a friend, you'll probably spend the whole time talking to them, but on your own you're more likely to meet local people. Some of my most sociable trips have been to places without many tourists. Talk to taxi drivers, waiters, shopkeepers – you'll get a lot of advice you can't find in guidebooks! On the whole, people are remarkably friendly and generous. One of the best holidays I've had was in a remote area of Turkey, where several people invited me for meals in their own homes.

And just imagine – no more boring art galleries when you'd rather be white-water rafting instead. And no more hanging around shops while your friend tries on fifteen different hats. Or if you just fancy spending the day under a tree with a book, there's nobody to complain!

It's worth giving yourself the flexibility to change your options. If you plan everything before you go, you can end up missing out on unexpected opportunities. You might get an invitation to somewhere wonderful, or you might decide you love a place and don't want to move on. But if you know you're going to arrive somewhere late in the evening, make sure you book a hotel in advance – you don't want to be wandering around strange streets at night with nowhere to go.

And what about women travellers? Well, they can and do have equally good experiences as men. That doesn't mean there aren't some risks. Obviously you shouldn't get in a car with someone you've just met, for example, but that's just common sense, isn't it? It's worth putting the number for the police in your phone. And be careful in cafés and bars to make sure nobody puts anything in your drink. Some unlucky travellers have woken up several hours later with no money or passport.

Finally, do your research before you go – find out about the local culture and social attitudes. How should you dress to avoid negative attention? Are there any typical tricks that thieves use on tourists?

So should we all be brave and try it? I definitely think so. The only danger I can see is that you may never want to go on holiday with your friends or family again!

City living

7A — **LANGUAGE**

GRAMMAR: Present perfect with *just*, *yet* and *already*

1 Order the words to make sentences. There may be more than one correct answer.

1 the / for / already / I've / tickets / paid

_____.

2 you / have / finished / essay / yet / your

_____?

3 it's / I've / 7 a.m. and / the house / cleaned / already

_____.

4 just / spoken / the phone / I've / to Carolina on

_____.

5 dinner / you / had / have / your / yet

_____?

6 got home / I've / from work and / I'm tired / just

_____.

7 already / done it / need to / you don't / go shopping / because I've

_____.

8 you / Pedro's girlfriend / yet / met / have

_____?

2 Complete the sentences with the verbs in the box. Use the present perfect and the words in brackets. There is one verb you don't need.

> eat   not open   spend   not make
> come   cycle   take

1 The bread's still warm. I _____ it out of the oven. (just)

2 I was going to have some chocolate, but you _____ it. (already)

3 Camila _____ any friends at her new school _____. (yet)

4 I gave both children €20 and they _____ it _____. (already)

5 I'm hot and sweaty because I _____ eight kilometres. (just)

6 They've built the new sports stadium, but they _____ it _____. (yet)

VOCABULARY: City features

3 Are the following sentences true (T) or false (F)?

1 You usually find bridges under the ground.   ____
2 You can make statues from stone.   ____
3 Traffic lights control the movement of cars.   ____
4 Fountains send water into the air.   ____
5 Apartment blocks are always low buildings.   ____
6 At a crossroads, one road meets another.   ____

4 Complete the words.

1 In towns and cities, it's safer to walk on the p__ __ __ __ __ __ __.

2 You can use a p__ __ __ __ __ __ __ __ __ crossing to get across the road.

3 Is there a l__ __ __ __ __ b__ __ that I can put this empty bottle in?

4 The road was very dark because there were no s__ __ __ __ __ l__ __ __ __ __.

5 We drove through a long t__ __ __ __ __ under the river.

6 Let's sit on this b__ __ __ __ to eat our sandwiches.

PRONUNCIATION: *just* and *yet*

5 ▶ 7.1 Listen to the sentences. Which sound do the underlined words start with? Write numbers 1–7 in the correct columns. Listen again and repeat.

/j/	/dʒ/
__ __ __ __	__ __ __

1 Is Alfonso here <u>yet</u>?
2 Have you already been to the <u>gym</u>?
3 Anna's <u>just</u> left secondary school.
4 Vinicius <u>usually</u> has dinner with us on Friday.
5 He's applied for a new <u>job</u>.
6 Hi! How are <u>you</u>?
7 They look so <u>young</u>!

LISTENING: Listening for facts and figures

1 Read the sentences from the audio about cycling. What type of information is missing? Match the gaps with a–f.

1 It's cheap, it's _____ and, more than anything, it's quick. _____

2 Of course, I love to walk, too, but if I go anywhere on foot, it _____ so long. _____

3 There are only about _____ people living here. _____

4 I can cycle from one end of town to the other in _____. _____

5 If I drive to work at _____ in the morning, it takes me half an hour. _____

6 If I cycle, I can get to the office at _____. _____

7 When I arrive somewhere, I don't have to find a _____. _____

8 All in all, I probably cycle for about _____ a week. _____

a time

b verb

c noun

d adjective

e duration of time

f number

2 ▶7.2 Listen and complete the gaps in exercise 1.

3 ▶7.3 Look at the example. Listen to these sentences. Mark where the /t/ sound links with the next word and where it is not pronounced.

1 Matt and I have already walk(ed) ten miles!

2 We gave Bret a lift to the station.

3 She missed the bus so she went on the train instead.

4 I've just seen Anna and Scott in the car park.

5 He picked up his bag and crossed the road.

4 Order the letters to make words to complete the sentences.

1 He drove around the car park twice, trying to find a KRAGNIP CASPE _____.

2 We stood on the FLAMTROP _____, waiting for the train to arrive.

3 If we ETS FOF _____ at nine o'clock, we should arrive at midday.

4 I'm driving to Maria's house so I could give you a FILT _____.

5 I usually cycle there. It takes too long to go NO TOFO _____.

6 We were stuck in a RACFFIT MAJ _____ for almost an hour.

7 My favourite form of BUPCLI PARTNORTS _____ is the bus.

8 HURS HURO _____ starts just before seven every morning.

9 The train was full of MOCMETURS _____ on their way to work.

10 If we leave now, we should get there NO MEIT _____.

GRAMMAR: Present perfect with *for* and *since*

1 Complete the sentences with *for* or *since*.

1 We've known Murat _____ over ten years.

2 I've been a member of this gym _____ 2014.

3 My parents haven't heard from Beyza _____ March.

4 Have you seen Ahmet _____ you arrived?

5 I've been waiting here_____ ages!

6 Aline has been ill _____ over three weeks now.

7 I haven't driven _____ I passed my test.

8 They've lived in the same apartment _____ years.

9 Paolo hasn't eaten meat _____ he was a child.

10 Have you two known each other _____ a long time?

2 Complete the questions and answers.

1 **A** How many years was she a teacher?
   B She _____ a teacher _____ three years.

2 **A** How long were you in hospital?
   B I _____ there _____ two months.

3 **A** How long _____ Gabriela _____ a vegetarian?
   B Ten years.

4 **A** How many years _____ you and Paolo _____ married?
   B Nearly five.

5 **A** How long _____ your father in the army?
   B From 1990 till 2005.

6 **A** How long _____ you study medicine for?
   B I studied _____ eight years – until 2014.

3 Use the prompts to write questions and answers. Use the present perfect form of the verbs with *for* or *since*.

1 **A** how long/you/live/in Madrid

   _____?

   B I/be/here/three years

   _____.

2 **A** how long/she/be/asleep

   _____?

   B she/be/asleep/5.30

   _____.

3 **A** how long/Luis/have/a cough

   _____?

   B he/have/it/the weekend

   _____.

4 **A** how long/your cousins/work/in France

   _____?

   B they/work there/over ten months

   _____.

PRONUNCIATION: *for* and *since*

4 ▶ 7.4 Practise saying the sentences. Are *for* and *since* stressed (S) or unstressed (U)? Listen, check and repeat.

1 I've been here for three hours. **S U**

2 She's felt ill since Wednesday. **S U**

3 We've known about it since midday. **S U**

4 Livia has lived in Paris for six months. **S U**

5 They haven't heard from her since April. **S U**

6 I haven't eaten since breakfast. **S U**

7 We haven't seen Maria for years. **S U**

8 She's been away since 2014. **S U**

WRITING: Writing an essay

1 Read Otto's essay and complete it with these linking words and phrases.

a The second reason
b In conclusion
c Firstly
d Finally

Should cars be banned from the city centre?

I live in a beautiful, historic city, but everyone agrees that there is a problem with traffic. Every day, over 60,000 people drive into the city centre for work or study, and pollution levels are rising. Our local council has suggested banning all cars from the city centre. Personally, I think this is a very bad idea.

1 _____, how would people get to work? Houses in the city are very expensive, and people who live outside the city already have long journeys to work. In my view, it is unreasonable that they should have to wait for a bus to travel into the city centre.

2 _____ is that I don't believe that it's possible for some people to use public transport or walk or cycle to work. For example, people in wheelchairs need special vehicles, and many people have to carry heavy tools or equipment for their work.

3 _____, I'm worried that local shops and businesses will suffer. If people can't drive to the shops, they won't come at all. Most people don't want to carry bags full of shopping on a bus.

4 _____, I feel that banning cars from the city centre is a bad idea. I would say that we should be looking at different ways of reducing pollution – ways that don't involve making life difficult for people! For example, we should develop better electric cars, improve public transport and make better cycle routes.

2 Find these phrases in Otto's essay. Then write sentences with your own ideas about whether or not cars should be banned from city centres.

1 Personally, _____.
2 In my view _____.
3 I don't believe that _____.
4 I'm worried that _____.
5 I would say that _____.

3 Use the words in the box to complete the arguments against Otto's opinion.

> fresh air   pollution   healthier
> public transport   permission   safe

1 In my opinion, banning cars would reduce _____.

2 I don't believe that it's _____ for cars and bicycles to share the road.

3 I think that getting some _____ by walking or cycling to work is a good idea.

4 People who need to carry heavy equipment could get _____ from the council to drive.

5 Personally, I feel that people who can't walk or cycle should use _____.

6 I wouldn't say that cycling is difficult for most people, and it makes them _____.

4 Write an essay giving the opposite opinion to Otto's.

- Use ideas from exercise 3 or your own ideas.
- Organize your ideas into five paragraphs: introduction, reasons 1–3, conclusion.
- Give examples or evidence to support your opinion.
- Use some of the phrases from exercise 2.

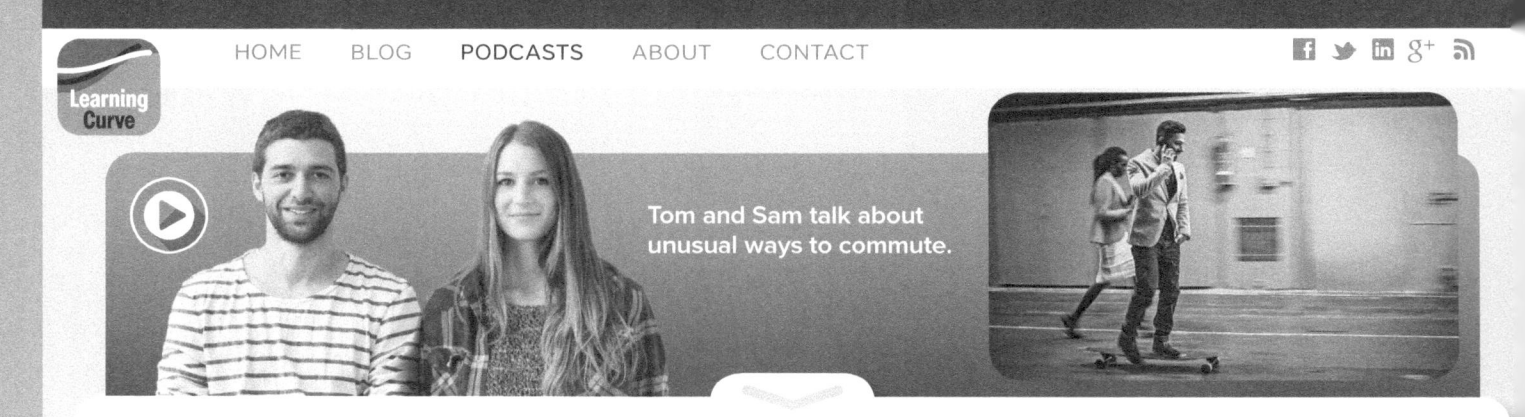

HOME   BLOG   PODCASTS   ABOUT   CONTACT

Tom and Sam talk about unusual ways to commute.

LISTENING

1 ▶ **7.5** Listen to the podcast. What does the speaker say is the main advantage of how he commutes?

a It's a healthy way to get to work.

b His journey is quicker than other people's.

c He can still wear a suit while he's travelling.

2 ▶ **7.5** Listen again. Complete the sentences with one or two words.

1 It takes Louie about _____ to get to work.

2 He rides his skateboard on the _____.

3 He has been skateboarding for _____ years.

4 He thinks other people are _____ of his journey to work.

5 He says the best thing about not using _____ is not waiting for buses.

6 He thinks skateboarding is less _____ than cycling.

7 He also uses his skateboard to go to _____.

READING

1 Read the blog about car-free cities. Match 1–4 with paragraphs A–D.

1 places where little is being done to reduce car use _____

2 how some cities have encouraged people not to drive _____

3 how technology can help people to manage without cars _____

4 a new city where people won't need to drive _____

2 Are the sentences true (T), false (F), or is there not enough information to decide (N)?

1 People often need to drive to other places on their way to and from work. _____

2 Most people who work in cities drive to work. _____

3 In Milan, most people travel by public transport once or twice a week. _____

4 London is a safe place to cycle to work. _____

5 In the new town near Chengdu, it will be easy for most people to walk everywhere. _____

6 Planners want people who work in Chengdu to drive there very quickly in their own cars. _____

7 It is easy for people in Helsinki to get information to help them travel without cars. _____

8 Most people in Helsinki already use public transport. _____

9 It is convenient for some people in US towns to cycle around their cities. _____

10 In Sydney, town planning makes it easy for people to use cars rather than public transport. _____

HOME   **BLOG**   PODCASTS   ABOUT   CONTACT

Guest blogger Penny writes about how cities are designed.

Car-free cities – dream or reality?

What's the number one thing you hate about cities? It's probably the traffic. Who wants to breathe in dirty air all day, or spend hours stuck in a traffic jam on their daily commute? On the other hand, we've had cars for over 100 years now and we rely on them, especially with our busy lives – rushing to drop the kids off at school before we go to work, or going to the supermarket on the way home. So how can town planners persuade us to leave our cars at home? Here are some different ideas from around the world.

A Since 2014 Milan has had a really interesting system – for every day a resident leaves their car at home, they get a voucher for the value of a ticket on the train or bus! And in Copenhagen around half of all workers commute by bike on a huge, safe network of bike lanes. Perhaps London should try to do the same – traffic there moves more slowly than the average cyclist, but the streets are far more dangerous on two wheels!

B In some countries, town planners working on new towns and cities are trying to reduce car use to the minimum possible before they've even been built. For example, one new town in China, with a planned population of 80,000, is being designed so that all its shops, entertainment venues, work places, etc. are within a fifteen-minute walk of where residents live. And there'll be fast public transport connections to the nearest big city of Chengdu.

C In Helsinki, local authorities are using phone apps to reduce car numbers. The city has several schemes for people to share the use of bikes and cars. The app allows anyone to quickly find the nearest shared bike, car, or taxi, or tells them the best and fastest bus or train route. Planners there hope that within ten years no one will need to drive in the city at all.

D Sadly, not all cities are encouraging car-free journeys. It's true that 60% of people living in Paris don't own a car, but many US towns are designed specifically for car use, and there aren't any alternatives yet. And in car-loving Sydney, things seem to be going backwards – there are plans to get rid of pedestrian space to make room for even more cars!

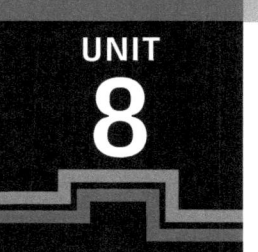

UNIT 8

Food for thought

8A LANGUAGE

GRAMMAR: *Too, too many, too much* and *(not) enough*

1 Match the pairs of sentences.

1 She needs a holiday. ____
2 I can't wear this jumper on a warm day. ____
3 She felt uncomfortable after the meal. ____
4 Can you open the window? ____
5 Let's put the heating on. ____
6 This coat's no good for winter. ____
7 She won't pass the exam. ____
8 She was hungry when she went to bed. ____

a She works too hard.
b It's too hot in here.
c It's not thick enough.
d She doesn't work hard enough.
e She didn't eat enough.
f It isn't hot enough in here.
g It's too thick.
h She ate too much.

2 Complete the conversation with *too, too many, too much* or *(not) enough*.

A I'm so worried about my exams. I haven't done ¹_____ work.

B I feel the same! I think I'm doing ²_____ subjects. I work late every evening, but then I'm ³_____ tired to concentrate in class.

A I'm especially worried about French. Our teacher doesn't explain things clearly ⁴_____ and he doesn't give us ⁵_____ time to write things down.

B My problem is History. There's ⁶_____ information to write and there's ⁷_____ time. I want to study History at university, and if my exam results aren't good ⁸_____, I won't be able to.

A Well, try not to worry about it ⁹_____!

B You're right. Getting ¹⁰_____ stressed won't help!

VOCABULARY: Food and drink

3 Order the letters to complete the words.

1 s __ __ __ __ __   MONAL
2 a __ __ __ __ __ __ __ __   BIERNUGE
3 p __ __ __ __   CHAE
4 a __ __ __ __ p __ __ __   EPPL EI
5 p __ __ __ __ __   PPSREE
6 f __ __ __ __ j __ __ __ __   TIUR CIUE
7 p __ __ __ __ __ __ __ __   EAINLEPP
8 t __ __ __ __ __ __ s __ __ __ __   MOOTA UACE
9 c __ __ __ __ __ __ __   UUMCREB
10 t __ __ __   NAU

4 Complete the crossword. The first letters and total number of letters are given.

¹P ²C ³T ⁴L ⁵C ⁶L ⁷F ⁸S ⁹C ¹⁰B

Across

4 meat from a sheep (4)
5 lots of people eat this for breakfast with milk (6)
8 a soft red fruit – you can make jam with it (10)
9 a fruit with a hard brown outside and a white part and liquid inside (7)
10 meat from a cow (4)

Down

1 a small, pink sea animal with a shell (5)
2 a vegetable with lots of green leaves; we usually cook it (7)
3 meat from a large bird (6)
6 a green salad vegetable (7)
7 we use this powder to make bread, cakes, etc. (5)

PRONUNCIATION: *too much sugar*

5 ▶ 8.1 Look at the underlined words. Listen and circle the vowel sound that you hear. Listen, check and repeat.

1 What <u>should</u> I do now?	/uː/	/ʌ/	/ʊ/
2 There aren't <u>enough</u> strawberries.	/uː/	/ʌ/	/ʊ/
3 I'm going to <u>cook</u> dinner.	/uː/	/ʌ/	/ʊ/
4 May I <u>use</u> your pen?	/uː/	/ʌ/	/ʊ/
5 Would you like a <u>cup</u> of coffee?	/uː/	/ʌ/	/ʊ/
6 I hate tomato <u>soup</u>!	/uː/	/ʌ/	/ʊ/
7 There wasn't any <u>food</u> left.	/uː/	/ʌ/	/ʊ/
8 Shall I <u>put</u> the heating on?	/uː/	/ʌ/	/ʊ/

READING: Scanning for specific information

Food stories

ABOUT US   RECIPES   INGREDIENTS   SHOP

Aquafaba ('Aqua what?!')

As regular readers of this blog will know, I know my food! I always say, give me a dish from pretty much anywhere in the world and, within two minutes, I'll tell you what's in it. However, this weekend, I discovered that maybe I don't know quite as much as I thought I did. A vegan friend of mine invited me over for dinner. (He turned vegan five years ago after seeing a really shocking movie on the dairy industry.) Just to remind you, vegans avoid all animal products, including honey. So I was expecting beans to be on the menu (and they were – lots of them – in the main course). But it was the dessert that took me by surprise – vegan ice cream. And how do you make ice cream, I hear you ask, without milk, cream or eggs? (I should say, how do you make nice, creamy ice cream without dairy products, because I've had some fairly unpleasant vegan ice creams in my time!) Well, it turns out that the key to good vegan ice cream – and a whole load of other desserts – is bean water. Yes, you read that correctly – bean water, i.e. the water that beans have been boiled in. (You know, the stuff you usually throw down the sink.) Bean water, my friend tells me, is called 'aquafaba' by the vegan community. It's increasingly used to replace egg whites in savoury and sweet vegan dishes, such as vegan butter, cheese, biscuits and cakes. And I can honestly say it works, although it does give the ice cream a slightly odd smell. It's so good, in fact, that the morning after my dinner date, I went straight to the supermarket for a tin of beans. As I write, my first batch of aquafaba ice cream is firming up nicely in the freezer!

1 <u>Underline</u> the key words in these questions. Then scan the text about an unusual food and choose the best answer.

1 What did the blogger's friend invite her over for?
   a dessert
   b dinner
   c a dish containing eggs

2 What do vegans avoid eating?
   a milk and eggs
   b honey and cream
   c all animal products

3 What was the blogger expecting to be given to eat?
   a beans
   b vegan ice cream
   c a dessert

4 What, according to the blogger, is the key to many good vegan desserts?
   a beans
   b bean water
   c cream

5 In vegan cooking, aquafaba is used to replace
   a cream.
   b egg whites.
   c dairy products.

2 Look at the sentences. Write T for true sentences, F for false sentences, and N when the article doesn't give you enough information to be sure.

1 The blogger is a vegetarian, not a vegan. _____
2 The blogger's vegan friend has never eaten animal products. _____
3 The main course of the meal included beans. _____
4 This was the first time the blogger had eaten vegan ice cream. _____
5 The blogger says that aquafaba is usually thrown away. _____
6 Aquafaba is much healthier than egg white. _____
7 She says the smell of this vegan ice cream is especially nice. _____
8 She has now tried making vegan ice cream with aquafaba herself. _____

3 Choose the correct linkers to complete the sentences. There may be more than one correct answer.

1 I liked the vegan ice cream, *however / but / although* I found the idea of bean water a little strange at first.

2 *Although / However / But* I'd tried lots of vegan ice creams, I'd never especially enjoyed them.

3 I don't have a recipe for the ice cream, *however / although / but* I'm going to follow my friend's instructions.

4 I usually know what's in a dish. *But / Although / However,* I have no idea what's in this.

5 I don't usually cook vegan food. *However / Although / But,* I feel inspired to try now.

GRAMMAR: *Must(n't)* and *(not) have to*

1 Choose the correct options to complete the sentences.

1 You ____ finish that pie if you don't want it.
a don't have to   b must   c mustn't

2 To pass this exam, you ____ score over 75%.
a mustn't   b don't have to   c must

3 You ____ talk to Peter because he has a lot of work to do.
a must   b don't have to   c mustn't

4 This is Ben's medicine. He ____ take it three times a day.
a mustn't   b have to   c has to

5 Do we ____ bring our own food?
a must   b don't have to   c have to

6 I have an important meeting. I ____ be late.
a don't have to   b mustn't   c have to

7 My new job is close to my house, so I ____ catch the train.
a mustn't   b don't have to   c have to

8 If you hear the fire alarm, you ____ leave the building immediately.
a don't have to   b mustn't   c must

9 Why are you going home? Do you ____ get up early tomorrow?
a have to   b must   c mustn't

10 It's Gina's birthday next week. I ____ forget to send her a card.
a don't have to   b mustn't   c must

2 Complete the sentences with *must, mustn't*, or the correct form of *(not) have to*. There may be more than one correct answer.

1 We're going for a walk, but you _____ come if you're too tired.

2 There are thieves in the area, so you _____ make sure your car is locked.

3 Does Harry _____ wear his uniform on the school trip?

4 We _____ swim here – it's too dangerous.

5 Marta is very rich, so she _____ work.

6 Larry is in a hurry because he _____ catch a bus in five minutes.

7 Do the children's parents _____ sign these forms?

8 We can leave the classroom at any time. We _____ ask for permission.

VOCABULARY: Adjectives to describe food

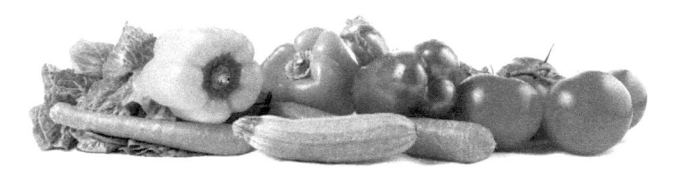

3 Complete the sentences with the adjectives in the box.

> creamy   salty   sour   healthy   sweet
> crunchy   bitter   delicious

1 A _____ diet should include plenty of fresh vegetables and fruit.

2 Alex is such a good cook. He made an absolutely _____ curry last week.

3 You shouldn't eat too many _____ foods like crisps and olives.

4 Someone left the biscuits out all night and they're not _____ any more.

5 The coffee was much too strong and had a rather _____ flavour.

6 Mira loves _____ foods like chocolate and cakes.

7 She served the apple pie with a lovely _____ sauce.

8 Add sugar to the lemon juice, otherwise it will taste too _____.

4 Complete the adjectives.

1 Laura put a lot of chillies in the soup and it was too s___ ___ ___ ___.

2 Rob forgot to take the potatoes out of the oven and they were b___ ___ ___ ___ ___.

3 You haven't cooked this chicken long enough – it's still r___ ___ in the middle!

4 Paul loves un___ ___ ___ ___ ___ ___y foods like pizza and burgers.

5 You can make a t___ ___ ___y soup with chicken bones.

6 Does the restaurant use f___ ___ ___ ___ vegetables from their own garden?

7 Bean ice cream? It sounds d___ ___ ___ ___ ___ ___ing!

8 I don't eat meat – are there any v___ ___ ___ ___ ___ ___ian dishes?

PRONUNCIATION: Sentence stress

5 ▶ 8.2 Practise saying the sentences, putting the main stress on the underlined modal verb. Listen, check and repeat.

1 You <u>must</u> bring your passport with you.

2 Do we <u>have</u> to leave tomorrow morning?

3 She <u>mustn't</u> take the hotel towels to the beach.

4 You don't <u>have</u> to wait if you don't want to.

5 Parents <u>mustn't</u> help their children with this homework.

6 She <u>has</u> to arrive there before 9 a.m.

SPEAKING: Making and responding to invitations

1 ▶8.3 Listen to the conversation between Karl and Brigit. Complete the phrases.

1 Do _____ trying that new Japanese restaurant tonight?

2 I'm _____ I've already got _____.

3 But would you be _____ the Japanese place another evening?

4 OK then, do you _____ go on Saturday instead?

5 Oh _____, I think _____ that evening.

6 Yeah. That would be _____, except I'll have to leave quite early.

7 Would _____ to stay over at my place?

8 That's _____ of you, thanks.

2 Are phrases 1–8 in exercise 1 used for inviting (I), accepting (A) or refusing (R)?

1 ____

2 ____

3 ____

4 ____

5 ____

6 ____

7 ____

8 ____

3 ▶8.4 Listen to four people refusing invitations. Tick (✔) the things each speaker does.

	Speaker 1	Speaker 2	Speaker 3	Speaker 4
Use pleasant intonation				
Apologize before saying something negative				
Give explanations				

4 ▶8.5 Read the conversation then complete what B says. There is more than one possible answer for each gap. Then listen and say B's part aloud.

A Would you be interested in going to the cinema on Saturday? There's a new action movie that's meant to be really good.

B ¹_____. My parents are having a party. It's been planned for a long time and I can't miss it.

A Oh sure, I understand. The movie's on all week though. Do you fancy going another night?

B ²_____. I read an online review and it sounds really exciting. Sunday's good for me.

A Great. Would you like to come round to my place for a quick dinner before we go?

B ³_____. Why don't I bring something for dessert?

A Excellent! See you then. Bye for now.

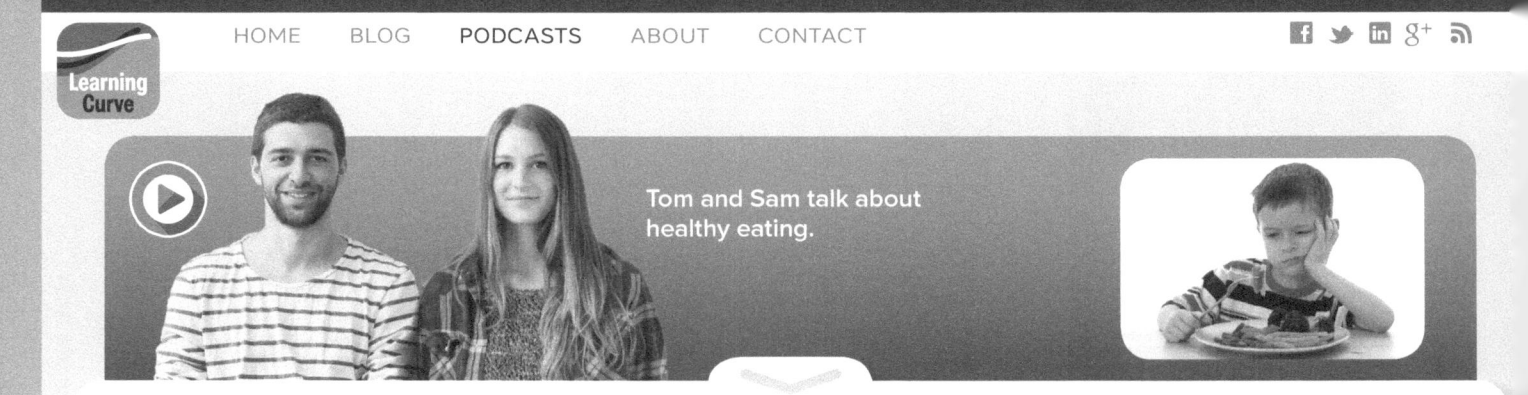

HOME   BLOG   PODCASTS   ABOUT   CONTACT

Tom and Sam talk about healthy eating.

LISTENING

1 ▶ 8.6 Listen to the podcast. Choose the best summary.

a Luca's diet is healthy now, but wasn't when he was younger.

b Luca and his brother have unhealthy diets now.

c Luca's diet has always been quite unhealthy.

2 ▶ 8.6 Listen again. Are the sentences true (T) or false (F)?

1 Luca's mother still tells him to eat more fish. _____

2 When he was younger, Luca ate a lot of vegetables. _____

3 Luca didn't use to like green vegetables. _____

4 Luca's mother made him eat everything on his plate. _____

5 Luca's brother doesn't like vegetables. _____

6 Luca eats uncooked vegetables. _____

7 Luca avoids food with a lot of salt in. _____

8 Luca eats unhealthy food while watching films. _____

9 Luca really dislikes fish. _____

10 Luca's favourite sauces contain a lot of cream. _____

READING

1 Read the blog about cooking. What does it suggest?

a Everyone can learn to cook well with the right instructions.

b There are lots of things that can go wrong when cooking.

c You need lots of equipment in order to cook successfully.

2 Choose the correct options, according to the information in the blog.

1 What is the advantage of cooking a vegetable soup?
   a It is healthy.
   b It is easy.
   c It is vegetarian.

2 Before you start cooking, what should you read?
   a the first line of the recipe
   b the first half of the recipe
   c the whole recipe

3 Which of these things should you check before starting to cook?
   a that you have the right equipment
   b what time it is
   c how many vegetables you need

4 What will a recipe <u>not</u> tell you?
   a which vegetables to use
   b what sort of knife you need
   c exactly how to prepare an onion

5 What does the word *concentrate* in line 20 mean?
   a to do something quickly
   b to focus on one activity
   c to be very careful

6 Why should you add stock to the soup?
   a to make it smell nice
   b to make it less hot
   c to improve the taste

7 What does the last line of the blog suggest?
   a You probably won't eat the soup.
   b You will really enjoy the soup.
   c You will definitely make the soup again.

HOME **BLOG** PODCASTS ABOUT CONTACT

Guest blogger Jack tells us how to stay calm in the kitchen.

Keep calm and cook on

If you're new to cooking and want some basic tips, here's a great recipe for a simple but delicious soup. I'll take you step by step through what to do – and what not to do!

1   The first piece of advice is, <u>always</u> read the instructions to the end before you start cooking. You don't want to find out halfway through that you don't have all
5   the ingredients (what if you've run out of noodles?), or some of the equipment (what if your neighbour doesn't own an ice-cream maker either?), or enough time to cook it (oh no, my girlfriend/boyfriend
10   will be here in five minutes and all I've got is a lot of raw vegetables!)

So, after you've read all the instructions, re-read the first line: 'Peel and slice the onion'. Take a sharp kitchen knife, and remove the first brown layer from the onion, and then the second (brownish) layer and then a third. Now, of course the recipe won't tell you when to stop and you
15   don't want to end up with a really tiny onion. Make sure you have plenty of other vegetables – a red pepper, a couple of carrots and a potato (even if slightly green). Chop them into small pieces (and don't worry about the green potato, no one will know once it's cooked).

Next, heat some oil in a pan. But how much oil? And what sort of pan? Pour in enough to just cover the bottom of a medium-sized saucepan. Then add the vegetables. At this point, whatever you do,
20   concentrate! Do not attempt to do anything else! Do not answer your phone! Ignore the doorbell (unless it's the firefighters)! It's so easy to forget to keep an eye on things. Turn the heat down and let the vegetables cook gently for a few minutes. (Don't they smell good?) Then add a litre of water, plus two big spoons of stock (you know, that mysterious salty brown powder at the back of the cupboard – it may not look much, but without it, your soup won't taste … anything like soup). Put
25   a lid on the pan, and leave it for half an hour.

Of course, at this point, you'll forget the instruction not to answer your phone, and will end up talking to a friend for an hour. The final step (nearly) is to taste the 'soup'. And when you discover that even your dog won't eat it … order a takeaway.
29   And that's why you should always read the instructions first!

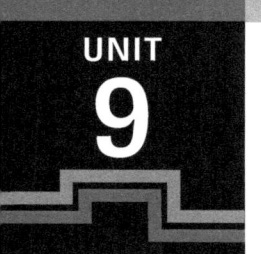

Money and shopping

9A   LANGUAGE

GRAMMAR: *used to*

1 Complete the sentences with the words and phrases in the box. You will need to use two of them twice.

> usually   use to   went   did   used to   go

1 Paolo looks different now. He didn't _____ have long hair.
2 On my sixth birthday, I _____ horse riding for the first time.
3 _____ you use to visit your cousins when you were younger?
4 I didn't use to _____ swimming as a child.
5 Yusuf _____ catches the bus to college.
6 She ate lots of ice cream as a child. She _____ love it!
7 Did Daniel _____ be so thin?
8 Lara doesn't _____ go skiing in the summer.

2 Complete the sentences with the correct form of *used to* and the verb in brackets.

1 I never ate olives as a child. I _____ them. (hate)
2 Did Matheus _____ so hard-working when he was younger? (be)
3 She _____ tennis in her teens, but doesn't now. (play)
4 My grandfather _____ a mobile phone. (not have)
5 Did your parents _____ you bedtime stories? (read)
6 I _____ bright colours in the past. (not wear)
7 Did you _____ the train to London? (take)
8 Aline _____ so much before she went to college. (not go out)

VOCABULARY: Money verbs

3 Order the letters to make money verbs.

1 We aren't rich. We can't **fardof** _____ to stay in that hotel.
2 This café's so expensive. They **ceragh** _____ €8 for a cup of coffee!
3 She has a good job and **searn** _____ more than her husband.
4 Don't forget to **apy kabc** _____ the money Daniel gave you.
5 Jack's going shopping because he **tog apid** _____ yesterday.
6 Don't **awest** _____ your salary on things that you don't need!

4 Complete the sentences with money verbs in the correct form.

1 Can I _____ some money to buy a concert ticket, please?
2 How much did you _____ on that new jacket?
3 I _____ my best friend €10 yesterday to buy lunch.
4 Their house is huge. It must be _____ a fortune.
5 Which _____ more – the blue shirt or the green one?
6 I'm trying to _____ a little money each month to buy a new car.

PRONUNCIATION: *used to/use to*

5 ▶9.1 Practise saying the sentences. Pay attention to *used to* and *use to*. Listen, check and repeat.

1 She didn't use to play tennis.
2 They used to love going to festivals.
3 Did you use to walk to school together?
4 We used to work out at the same gym.
5 He didn't use to like classical music.
6 I remember that you used to enjoy dancing.

LISTENING: Identifying attitude and opinion

1 ▶ **9.2** Listen to Tom and Natalie talking about shopping. Are these sentences true (T) or false (F)?

1 Tom likes shopping online. _____
2 Natalie prefers online shopping. _____
3 Tom thinks online shopping is easy. _____
4 Natalie doesn't like department stores. _____

2 Are the underlined phrases from the conversation opinion (A), feeling (B) or attitude (C)?

1 Yeah, I do most of my shopping online – <u>I much prefer it</u>. _____
2 Sure, <u>you see</u> it's so convenient to shop online. _____
3 I mean, <u>to be honest</u>, shopping for clothes online is the opposite of convenient. _____
4 <u>I wouldn't say</u> that's a big problem. _____
5 I get really <u>fed up</u> waiting! _____
6 I guess <u>I just like shops</u>, especially department stores. _____
7 <u>I enjoy</u> wandering from the clothes section to the kitchen. _____
8 I just remember the crowds and the queues – it was <u>really boring</u>! _____

3 ▶ **9.2** Listen again and number the fillers 1–8 in order.

a like _____
b I mean _____
c kind of _____
d Er _____
e Well _____
f you see _____
g sort of _____
h So _____

4 ▶ **9.2** Listen again and complete these sentences and phrases with fillers from exercise 3.

1 Sure, _____, it's so convenient.
2 _____, you just return it, don't you?
3 It's _____ convenient because you don't have to leave your home.
4 You can _____ get everything you want under one roof.
5 And, _____, you can pick things up and see them and feel them.

5 Complete the sentences with shopping words.

1 That jacket was only thirty dollars? Wow! That's an absolute b___ ___ ___ ___ ___ ___!
2 I bought this bag in the s___ ___ ___ ___ for half the usual price!
3 Students get a d___ ___ ___ ___ ___ ___ ___ of 20% in all our shops.
4 The trousers didn't fit so I sent them back and got a r___ ___ ___ ___ ___.
5 I asked the shop assistant if I could e___ ___ ___ ___ ___ ___ ___ the jacket for a larger size.
6 Are you paying with cash or by c___ ___ ___ ___ ___ card?
7 I need to try this suit on. Where's the nearest c___ ___ ___ ___ ___ ___ ___ room?
8 Sometimes I used to go w___ ___ ___ ___ ___ shopping with no money in my pocket. I just looked at all the lovely things.
9 There was such a long q___ ___ ___ ___ to pay that I decided not to wait.
10 I paid for the items and the cashier gave me a r___ ___ ___ ___ ___ ___.

GRAMMAR: The passive

1 Choose the correct options to complete the sentences.

1 The wallet was _____ yesterday by a member of the public.
   a hand in   b handed in   c to hand in

2 This park _____ by many people.
   a isn't used   b isn't using   c doesn't use

3 When was the problem _____?
   a discovering   b discovered   c discover

4 In summer, dinner _____ in the garden.
   a served   b is served   c serving

5 A number of mistakes _____ during the investigation.
   a was made   b made   c were made

6 Over 300 people _____ to the party.
   a were invited   b invited   c was invited

2 Complete the text about the history of money. Use the present or past passive form of the verbs in brackets.

It ¹_____ (say) by many people today that 'money makes the world go round'. It's certainly hard to imagine life without it, but money ²_____ (not invent) until several thousand years ago in China. Tiny models of weapons and tools ³_____ (use) there as money. Before that, full-size tools and weapons ⁴_____ (exchange) for goods and services in a system called 'barter'. The first coins ⁵_____ (produce) 2,500 years ago in Lydia, in what is now Turkey. They ⁶_____ (make) from 'electrum', a mixture of gold and silver. The first paper banknotes ⁷_____ (print) by the Chinese at around the same time. Fast forward in time, and today most goods and services ⁸_____ (buy) with credit and debit cards, or even using smartphone 'wallets'. Huge sums ⁹_____ (send) from bank to bank without anyone touching a single banknote. Virtual currencies like Bitcoin ¹⁰_____ (accept) in some shops and online. Will notes and coins disappear completely within our lifetime?

3 Complete the sentences with the passive form of the verbs in the box. Use the tense in brackets.

discover eat write invent
wash bake steal paint

1 The planet Uranus _____ by Sir William Herschel in 1781. (past simple)

2 Bread _____ every morning in our own bakery. (present simple)

3 I don't have a bike now. It _____ last week from outside the school. (past simple)

4 The picture _____ by Pablo Picasso in 1933. (past simple)

5 His car always looks perfect because it _____ every week. (present simple)

6 This song _____ by John Grant. (past simple)

7 Lunch _____ in the main dining room. (present simple)

8 The first electric train _____ by a German in 1879. (past simple)

PRONUNCIATION: Sentence stress

4 ▶9.3 Underline the three words that you think will be stressed in each sentence. Listen, check and repeat.

1 This soup is made with peppers.
2 The children are taught by their parents.
3 These plants are grown by my father.
4 The message was posted on Facebook.
5 Those houses were built in 1975.
6 That race was won by her cousin.

WRITING: Writing a formal email

1 Read Elisabeth's email complaining about a flat-screen TV she has bought. Choose the correct words and phrases.

○ ○ ○

To: info@tvs2go.com

RE: Recent order (H23 100-A)

[1]*Dear Sir/Madam / Hello,*

I am writing [2]*to tell you about / with regard to* the flat-screen TV that [3]*a man installed / was installed* in my house last Thursday.

Firstly, [4]*someone delivered the TV / the TV was delivered* at 3 p.m., not at 10 a.m. as agreed. Secondly, as the man left, I noticed that some wires were hanging down at the back of the TV. When I [5]*pointed this out / told him about it*, he was extremely rude. Although he agreed to fix the wires, he [6]*did not / didn't* check that the TV was working correctly.

[7]*I'm / I am* sure you will agree that this level of service is [8]*terrible / unacceptable*, and that a full refund of the delivery charge would be appropriate. Could you please arrange [9]*to pay the money / for the money to be paid* within a week?

I look forward to hearing from you soon.

[10]*Regards / Bye for now*

Elisabeth Miller

2 Match the correct options 1–10 from exercise 1 with these features of formal emails.

a full forms, not contractions ___ ___

b formal words and expressions ___ ___ ___

c passives to avoid being personal ___ ___ ___

d a formal greeting ___

e a formal ending ___

3 Complete the sentences with nouns made from these verbs.

> order argue increase deliver
> improve discover discuss
> decide organize inform

1 Last week I made the _____ to purchase several items from your website.

2 The _____ on your website was not correct.

3 I was not aware of the price _____ when I ordered the product.

4 I was shocked by the _____ that several parts were broken.

5 After a _____ with one of your staff, I am still not satisfied.

6 I did not expect to become involved in an _____ with one of your sales team.

7 Poor service will damage the reputation of your _____.

8 Your company needs to make a great _____ in the quality of its goods.

9 I will expect _____ of a replacement within a week.

10 Please send me a full refund for my _____.

4 Write a formal email complaining about a product you have bought recently.

• Include paragraphs giving the reason for writing, explaining the situation and saying what action you want taken.

• Remember to use the features in exercise 2.

• Use the sentences in exercise 3 for ideas.

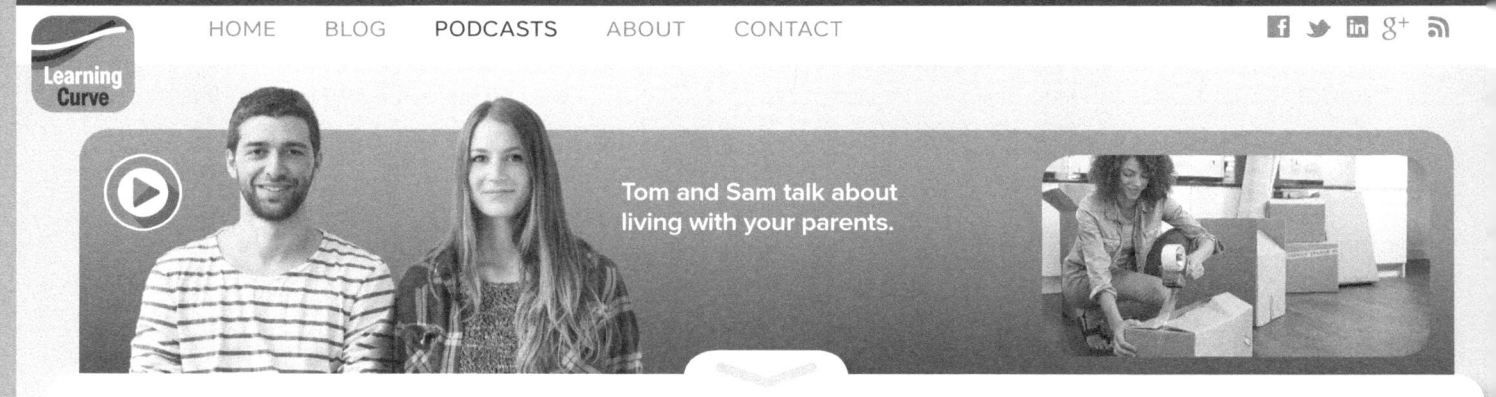

HOME   BLOG   PODCASTS   ABOUT   CONTACT

Tom and Sam talk about living with your parents.

LISTENING

1 ▶ 9.4 Listen to the podcast. Tick (✔) the correct statement.

a Sonia moved out of her parents' house because there were too many rules. _____

b Sonia's parents gave her money to help with her college fees. _____

c Sonia went to live with her parents because she wasn't earning enough money. _____

d Sonia couldn't afford to go to college so she got a job instead. _____

2 ▶ 9.4 Listen again. Complete the sentences with one or two words.

1 One of the _____ of Sonia's life was getting her degree.

2 Sonia was scared that she might trip and _____.

3 Sonia didn't know how she was going to _____ her college fees.

4 Sonia owed a total of _____ euros.

5 It took Sonia _____ to get a good job.

6 Sonia gave her parents money for _____ and _____.

7 When she was _____, Sonia didn't like her parents' rules.

READING

1 Read the blog about money and relationships. Choose the best summary.

a People often split up because they can't agree about money. You should talk about money with your partner, and if you have very different attitudes, it's best not to get married.

b It's hard to change people's attitudes to money, but if you understand how your partner feels, you won't feel so angry if they waste money you wanted to save.

c Attitudes to money are very important. You should try to understand how your partner feels and if you have different attitudes, you should try to find ways to stop them causing arguments.

2 Tick (✔) the correct sentences, according to the information in the blog.

1 Things that happen in our lives can affect how we feel about money. _____

2 Attitudes to money are more important than someone's personality. _____

3 People from poor families may not feel happy about borrowing money. _____

4 Attitudes to money can change if a relationship lasts a long time. _____

5 Couples should be honest with each other when they talk about money. _____

6 We should discuss the emotional reasons why money is important to us. _____

7 People with very different attitudes to money can't have a successful relationship. _____

8 Each person in a couple should pay the same amount of the bills. _____

9 Philip and Christa wanted to buy a home together. _____

10 When Philip saw Christa spending a lot of money, he thought their relationship wouldn't work. _____

HOME   BLOG   PODCASTS   ABOUT   CONTACT

Tom writes about money and relationships.

Money – how to stop it ruining your relationship

Experts say that the main reason long-term couples split up is money – and the arguments it causes. Our attitudes to money often come from our life experiences – and that makes them difficult to change. Someone brought up in a poor family may get really anxious about owing money, and be horrified at the idea of 'wasting' it on things they don't think are necessary. So what can we do to stop money ruining a relationship?

'We all have a money personality,' says life coach Jo Handslip. 'If we're thinking of a long-term relationship with someone, we need to get to know that side of them just as well as the other parts of their character. And whatever we may hope, we also need to understand that their money personality isn't likely to change.'

The most important thing a couple can do is talk about money openly. 'This isn't about money simply as a means of buying things,' says Jo. 'It's about what money represents to us.' She says that couples should start by trying to identify what each of them associates with money, like success, security, independence, power, fun or being free from stress.

Once they understand this, they can try to make their different attitudes work together. So, if one of you loves the freedom and excitement of spending money and the other one wants the security of having savings, maybe you should agree to share the cost of bills, but keep the rest of your money separate. That way, the 'spender' can only spend their own money, and the 'saver' can feel secure. Or you could agree a maximum amount you can spend without asking your partner.

Philip Walker knows all about the problems money can cause. He and his girlfriend Christa split up just two weeks before their wedding! 'We were saving up for a flat, so we agreed that the ceremony should be fairly small. But then I found out that instead of spending our savings on the wedding, Christa was going out celebrating with her friends in expensive clubs, and buying loads of new clothes when she already had more than she needed. She'd buy the same dress or pairs of shoes in three different colours because she couldn't decide which she liked best! We ended up having a huge argument. In the end, seeing her throw our money away made me feel that she didn't see a future for us together.'

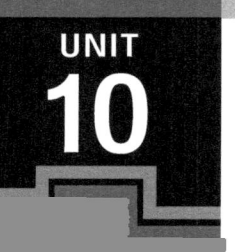

UNIT 10 Sport and fitness

10A LANGUAGE

GRAMMAR: Past perfect

1 Choose the correct tenses to complete the sentences.

1 That evening, I was tired because I _____ ten kilometres in the afternoon.
   a had run   b ran   c was running

2 We _____ hungry because we'd already eaten.
   a weren't being   b hadn't been   c weren't

3 By the time we arrived at the theatre, the play_____.
   a had already started   b already started
   c was already starting

4 When I met Lara I was sure I _____ her somewhere before.
   a saw   b was seeing   c had seen

5 I'd put on a thick jacket and I _____ too hot later.
   a was being   b had been   c was

6 I _____ how the movie would end because I had read the book.
   a had known   b knew   c know

7 He had cut his finger as he _____ the meat.
   a was preparing   b preparing   c had prepared

8 We arrived late at the party, so most of the food _____.
   a had gone   b went   c was going

9 I didn't have any money with me as I _____ my wallet.
   a didn't bring   b hadn't brought
   c wasn't bringing

10 Camilla said she had met Igor while she _____ around Europe.
   a travelled   b was travelling   c had travelled

2 Complete the sentences with the verb pairs. Write one past simple and one past perfect form in each sentence.

| say / go   live / move   know / go   meet / know |
| pass / study   be / lose   finish / leave   be / leave |

1 After we _____ our dinner, we _____ the restaurant.

2 The teacher _____ cross because I _____ my work at home.

3 He _____ stressed because he _____ his phone.

4 Jorge _____ all his exams because he _____ hard all year.

5 I _____ Javier once at Laura's house, so I _____ who he was.

6 She _____ in Italy for three years before she _____ to France.

7 Eduardo _____ most of the people at the club because he _____ there before.

8 After I _____ goodnight, I _____ to bed.

VOCABULARY: Sports and competitions

3 Order the letters to make words that match the definitions.

1 to behave dishonestly in order to achieve something THEAC _____

2 someone who watches people playing sport TRAPECOTS _____

3 to win a point CROSE _____

4 someone who does sports like running and jumping THELATE _____

5 the person who controls the game FREEREE _____

6 a prize for winning a competition HOTPRY _____

4 Complete the words.

1 She hopes to get a gold m___ ___ ___ ___ at the next Olympics.

2 Our team needs another goal to d___ ___ ___ the match.

3 There was a huge c___ ___ ___ ___ watching last night's game.

4 Don't forget to w___ ___ ___ u___ before you go running.

5 Would you like to t___ ___ ___ p___ ___ ___ in our swimming competition?

6 You can't g___ ___ ___ u___ now. You're nearly at the finishing line!

PRONUNCIATION: 'd/hadn't

5 ▶10.1 Practise saying the sentences. Pay attention to the pronunciation of 'd and hadn't. Listen, check and repeat.

1 She'd already won the match.
2 He hadn't taken part in the competition.
3 We'd lost both games.
4 They certainly hadn't cheated.
5 We hadn't scored yet.
6 They'd drawn in the semi-final.

READING: Finding information in a text

WEARABLE FITNESS DEVICES

Q 🔍 f 🐦 📷 g+ 📶

News
Reviews
Fitness trackers
Watches
Forum

Fitness trackers

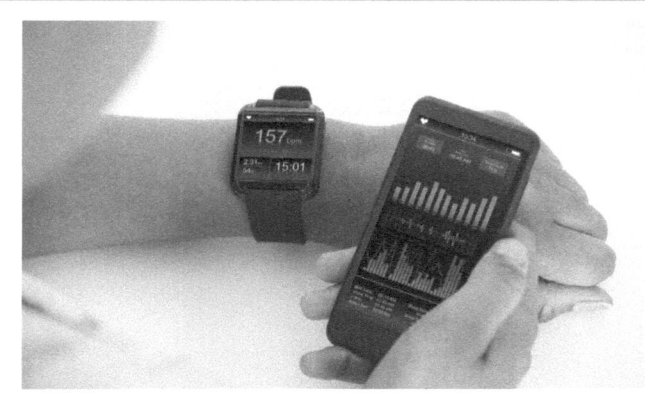

A | Wearable fitness is everywhere you look. There are now hundreds of types of fitness tracker on the market, the simplest of which simply count how many steps you take in a day. The more sophisticated models record your heartbeat, your food intake, your skin temperature, even how often you snore in your sleep! They allow you to observe and measure details about your own body that previously only doctors were able to see. Which, of course, is fascinating. But apart from providing interest in our lives, are these (often expensive) gadgets worth it? Do they serve any real purpose, other than making a nice profit for a number of companies?

B | Well, it turns out that in a lot of cases they probably do. Not because fitness trackers provide 100% accurate data. (If you try out two different brands of fitness tracker, it's very likely that you'll get two quite different step counts over the course of the day.) But because they're always there – often on your wrist – reminding you that you haven't moved or slept enough recently. Turn on your phone and a figure will pop up, telling you how well you're doing. (Some models will even tell you how well your friends are doing!) And that's what most of us need – a constant reminder that we need to do better.

C | And let's not forget that they're fun. Without a fitness tracker, we may know that we should use our legs more and our wheels less, but we may not actually do anything about it. When we wear a device that rewards us with a 'ping' every time we reach our target step count, we are more likely to get off the bus two stops away from work and walk. Daily routines become a sort of game we play with ourselves, and who wouldn't that appeal to?

1 Read the text about gadgets that measure your fitness, then match paragraphs A–C with three of summaries 1–6.

1 A disadvantage of wearable fitness devices. _____

2 What do fitness trackers do? _____

3 The companies that make these fitness devices. _____

4 The enjoyment factor of wearable fitness devices. _____

5 The author's experience of these fitness devices. _____

6 Why wearable fitness devices are useful. _____

2 Read the questions and match them to paragraphs A–C. Then write short answers. There are two questions for each paragraph.

1 What part of the body do you wear some of these devices on? _____

2 What do we all know we should do less of? _____

3 How many different kinds of device are available? _____

4 Where can you look at the information these devices collect? _____

5 What activity do we know we should do more often? _____

6 What can some devices count while you are in bed? _____

3 Complete the sentences with *example*, *for*, *like* or *such*.

1 We can all get more exercise, _____ instance, by walking rather than driving.

2 With this device daily routines, _____ going upstairs and walking home from the station, can be fun.

3 Everyone can now monitor aspects of their body's behaviour, _____ as their heartbeat and temperature.

4 We can find out, for _____, how deeply we're sleeping.

GRAMMAR: Reported speech

1 Complete the sentences with *said* or *told*.

1 She _____ she would call me at the weekend.

2 Nerea and Lucia _____ me they had seen you at the gym.

3 She _____ me that Gabriel had gone to the meeting.

4 He _____ that Yasmin would take Lola to the airport.

5 Isaac _____ he would talk to Miguel about the problem.

6 He _____ that Sophia liked her colleagues.

7 Paula _____ me she had met you at the wedding.

8 He _____ me that Livia wasn't coming.

2 Use the prompts to rewrite the sentences in reported speech.

1 'I'll phone you from the station.'
My sister / tell me / she phone me / from the station
_____.

2 'Dad can cook dinner for you and Laura.'
My mum / say / Dad cook / dinner for us
_____.

3 'I didn't see Luke in town on Saturday.'
He / tell me / he / not see / Luke in town on Saturday
_____.

4 'I've just bought a new computer.'
Maria / say / she buy / a new computer
_____.

5 'We're going to move to France.'
He / tell me / they going to move / to France
_____.

6 'I haven't made up my mind.'
She / say / she / not make up / her mind
_____.

7 'I'm meeting Davi on Friday.'
Vitor / tell me / he meet Davi / on Friday
_____.

8 'Alba loves going for walks.'
He / say / Alba love / going for walks
_____.

VOCABULARY: Parts of the body

3 Match parts of the body a–j with the definitions 1–8.

1 This is in your head and controls how you think. _____

2 This helps your arm to bend. _____

3 These are the soft edges of the mouth. _____

4 This helps your leg to bend. _____

5 This part of the body contains the heart. _____

6 This is the soft part of the front of the body, above your legs. _____

7 These are the two parts of your body at the tops of your arms. _____

8 This is just above your foot at the bottom of your leg. _____

a	shoulders	e	stomach	i	elbow
b	thumb	f	lips	j	knee
c	chest	g	forehead		
d	brain	h	ankle		

4 Complete the words.

1 After running, the m___ ___ ___ ___ ___ ___ in my legs were tired.

2 She'd broken a b___ ___ ___ in her foot and couldn't walk.

3 Azra was wearing a pretty scarf around her n___ ___ ___.

4 A healthy diet and regular exercise is good for your h___ ___ ___ ___ .

5 He was wearing sandals, so I could see his t___ ___ ___.

6 After a few days in the sun, her s___ ___ ___ was really brown.

7 Why is she pointing a f___ ___ ___ ___ ___ at me?

8 Vito has an expensive-looking watch on his left w___ ___ ___ ___.

PRONUNCIATION: Weak form of *that*

5 ▶ 10.2 Listen to the sentences. Is *that* strong (S) or weak (W)? Listen, check and repeat.

1 Zeynep said that she was leaving. _____

2 Is that your cousin over there? _____

3 That's not what I said! _____

4 Ismail told me that I was wrong. _____

5 Pam said that the party started at eight. _____

6 Could you give me that book, please? _____

7 Beatriz told Clara that she was angry. _____

8 Sara likes the blue bike, but I like that one. _____

SPEAKING: Making enquiries

1 ▶10.3 Gabriella is a guest at an expensive hotel. Listen to her conversation with the receptionist. Are the statements true (T) or false (F)?

1 Gabriella didn't know that the hotel has a fitness suite. _____

2 The exercise room has a lot of equipment that guests can use. _____

3 Gabriella wants someone to show her the exercise suite. _____

4 Guests don't have to pay to use the swimming pool. _____

5 The swimming pool is closed at night. _____

6 The receptionist will send an extra towel to Gabriella's room. _____

2 ▶10.3 Listen again. You will hear seven of these phrases. Write G (Gabriella) or R (receptionist).

a Is there anything else I can help you with? _____

b Could you give me some information about ..., please? _____

c Just one more thing. _____

d Excuse me, could you tell me ...? _____

e I'd also like to ask about ... _____

f Does that sound OK? _____

g I was told ... Is that true? ... _____

h I'll ... if you want. _____

i Shall I ...? _____

j Can I just double-check? Do you ...? _____

k Would you like me to ...? _____

l Could I speak to someone about ...? _____

m I was hoping you could help me. _____

3 Put the phrases from exercise 2 into the correct categories.

1 starting an enquiry politely _____ _____ _____ _____

2 asking for additional information _____ _____ _____ _____

3 being helpful _____ _____ _____ _____

4 ▶10.4 Use the phrases in exercise 2 to complete these conversations. There may be more than one possible answer. Then listen and say the missing part aloud.

1 In a sports shop

A Good morning. Can I help you?

B Hello. ¹_____ trainers, please? I'm looking for a pair for long-distance running.

A Yes, we have several suitable pairs. Shall I bring some for you to try?

B That would be great, thanks. ²_____ waterproof jackets.

A We don't have any available at the moment, but here's a catalogue. You can order them online. Does that sound OK?

2 At the gym

A Excuse me, can I get Pilates lessons here?

B Yes, we have several teachers. ³_____ give you a list?

A Great, thanks.

B You can call them to arrange a time. ⁴_____?

A Yes, perfect, thanks.

B Here's the list. ⁵_____?

A No, that's everything. Thanks for your help.

HOME BLOG PODCASTS ABOUT CONTACT

Learning Curve

Tom and Sam talk about joining a gym.

LISTENING

1 ▶ 10.5 Listen to the podcast. Tick (✔) the parts of the body which are mentioned.

a foot _____
b neck _____
c muscle _____
d ankle _____
e wrist _____
f stomach _____
g shoulder _____
h bone _____
i heart _____
j knee _____

2 ▶ 10.5 Listen again. Choose the correct options to complete the sentences.

1 How long has Hakim been going to the sports centre?
  a about one year
  b about two years
  c about five years

2 For his height, Hakim
  a weighs too little.
  b weighs the right amount.
  c weighs too much.

3 Hakim wants a workout that's good for his
  a stomach.
  b muscles.
  c heart.

4 Hakim says that he
  a has always been active.
  b has never done much exercise.
  c has never injured himself.

5 Hakim had to have an operation when he was
  a eight.
  b eleven.
  c twenty.

6 What happened while Hakim was skiing?
  a He got an injury to his leg.
  b He damaged part of his arm.
  c He caused a serious accident.

READING

1 Read the blog about sports injuries. Choose the best summary.

a Peter didn't prepare properly for his run and, because of his injury, he will never be able to run again.

b Peter hadn't realized there was a problem with his ankle and made things worse by doing more exercise.

c Peter wasn't used to doing much exercise, and badly hurt his ankle soon after starting his run.

2 Choose the correct options to complete the sentences.

1 According to Peter, after a sports injury you feel
  a upset and annoyed.
  b surprised and frightened.
  c tired and embarrassed.

2 Peter hurt his ankle
  a when he got up one day.
  b while he was running.
  c when he was preparing to run.

3 Peter's doctor told him
  a to stop running for a few weeks.
  b to run shorter distances.
  c to stop running completely.

4 Peter had
  a had a few injuries in the past.
  b never injured himself before.
  c only recently started running.

5 Peter says that stress
  a means it takes longer to recover from injury.
  b is hard for most people to control.
  c can make it difficult for him to run.

6 Peter says that he
  a thought his ankle would never get better.
  b was impatient to recover as quickly as possible.
  c did what his doctor had told him to do.

HOME **BLOG** PODCASTS ABOUT CONTACT

Guest blogger Kate gets some advice on recovering from sports injuries.

How I got back on track

We all know we should do plenty of exercise and many of us have a favourite sport or activity. But what happens if you suffer an injury and can't do the sport you love? How do you cope with it and how do you recover from it? Peter Jackson, sports coach and runner, told us about his experience of being injured.

It's tough. You feel so many negative emotions. You're angry because you can't do your sport. You feel disappointed because your body has failed you. And you're bored because you can't do what you want to do!

One morning last year I got up and noticed a problem with my right ankle. It was a slight pain at first and I thought it would go away. I'd done a long run the day before – a few miles more than usual – and thought perhaps that was why. Anyway, I went running, as usual. I'd done everything properly to prepare. I'd put a bandage on for support and, of course, I'd warmed up before starting.

But as I ran, the pain got worse and worse and after three miles I had to give up and go home. The next day, I saw my doctor who told me that I'd injured my ankle quite badly and that I would have to rest it for four to six weeks – that meant no running at all! It was a bit of a shock. Until that point, I'd run every day for the previous four or five years, with no problems. Suddenly, I had to learn new habits. Most importantly, I had to start listening to my body – it was telling me to rest.

Of course, at first I felt very stressed by not being able to run, but I learned to manage that. It's often said that stress is caused by the feeling that we can't control a situation, and stress stops the body from getting better. So the first thing I had to understand was that I was in control because I was helping myself to get better. I couldn't take part in running any more, but by resting my ankle and doing the exercises that the doctor had shown me, I was taking part in my recovery. I learned to be patient – to accept that it takes time to get better – and above all, I learned to be positive – to believe that I would recover.

UNIT 11 — At home

11A LANGUAGE

GRAMMAR: *-ing*/infinitive verb patterns

1 Choose the correct options to complete the sentences.

1 I have arranged _____ Rino this evening.
   a meeting   b to meet

2 Have you finished _____ your bedroom yet?
   a decorating   b to decorate

3 Frankie can't stand _____ early.
   a getting up   b to get up

4 The firm is planning _____ its factory in Ireland.
   a closing   b to close

5 Oh no! I forgot _____ my passport!
   a bringing   b to bring

6 Would you mind _____ dinner tonight?
   a cooking   b to cook

7 Gary hopes _____ a place in the team.
   a getting   b to get

8 Do you fancy _____ to the beach today?
   a going   b to go

9 I can't imagine _____ a marathon!
   a running   b to run

10 Unfortunately, I can't afford _____ a holiday this year.
   a having   b to have

2 Complete the text with the correct form of the verbs in the box.

> get   move   tell   play
> visit   stay   hang out   pay

Last year, I decided ¹_____ to another city. I was bored with my job, and I wanted a change. I'm the sort of person that hates ²_____ in the same place for too long. Luckily, I managed ³_____ a new job quite quickly. My new firm even offered ⁴_____ my rent for three months while I looked for a place to buy. The only problem was my great friend, Sol. He kept ⁵_____ me that I would be lonely and that I'd miss ⁶_____ with him and our other friends. I did feel sorry about leaving Sol, but I knew I'd make new friends quite quickly. I love ⁷_____ football and joining a team is always a good way to meet people. However, I promised ⁸_____ Sol as often as I could, and I've kept my promise.

VOCABULARY: Household objects

3 Order the letters to make words that match the descriptions.

1 It keeps you warm in bed. EVTUD   _____

2 It is in the bathroom and holds water. SHAW INSAB   _____

3 You put dirty clothes in it. GASWNHI CHANMIE   _____

4 You keep your clothes in it. THESC FO REWARDS

   _____

5 They are made of thin material and go on a bed. THESES   _____

6 It keeps your house warm. ANCTLER THIGANE

   _____

4 Complete the crossword.

			1						
				2					
3							4		
5									
					6				
7									
					8				
9									

Across

3 All the dirty plates need to go in the _____.

7 I sleep best with a soft _____ under my head.

8 The cake must be cooked, so take it out of the _____.

9 It was cold, so we put an extra _____ on the bed.

Down

1 If you're not comfortable on the sofa, put a _____ behind your back.

2 Pia had a _____ full of beautiful clothes.

4 A _____ is a small carpet.

5 I turned on both _____ to fill the bath quickly.

6 Is the _____ hot enough yet to do my shirt?

PRONUNCIATION: Sentence stress

5 ▶ 11.1 Listen to these sentences and repeat them. Pay attention to the way *to* is pronounced.

1 Guy can't afford to buy a new laptop.

2 The children enjoy playing in the park.

3 We plan to meet our friends at eight.

4 I don't fancy going to the cinema.

5 I forgot to lock the door.

6 Sylvie doesn't want to come with us.

LISTENING: Understanding and interpreting information

1 ▶**11.2** Read the sentences and look at the underlined words. Think about other words that the speakers might use. Then listen to the conversation. Are the sentences True (T) or False (F)?

1 Johnny is <u>extremely tired</u> after doing the housework. ____

2 Johnny has <u>cleaned</u> the kitchen floor. ____

3 Marta says Johnny's housemates will be <u>very pleased</u> with him. ____

4 As part of Marta and Sara's <u>agreement</u>, Marta cleans the house. ____

5 Marta tells Johnny she <u>hates</u> cleaning. ____

6 Marta's housemate, Sara, <u>is extremely keen on</u> food. ____

7 Marta says the meals that she cooks are <u>really good</u>. ____

8 Marta says she spends <u>a lot of time</u> deciding what to cook. ____

2 ▶**11.2** Listen again and check and write the actual words the speakers use.

1 extremely tired _____

2 cleaned _____

3 very pleased _____

4 agreement _____

5 hates _____

6 is extremely keen on _____

7 really good _____

8 a lot of time _____

3 Read the short conversations. Write the words that the speakers don't say.

1 A She was angry.
  B No, she wasn't. _____

2 A Do you think Maria's happy at work?
  B Not so sure about that! _____

3 A What's wrong?
  B Computer's not working! _____

4 A You look really stressed.
  B Yes! Big problem with the arrangements for Saturday! _____

5 A Sara doesn't like cooking, I'm guessing?
  B No, hates it! _____

4 Match a–e with missing words 1–5 in exercise 3.

a pronouns ____

b articles ____

c *be* and auxiliary verbs ____

d *There is/are* ____

e avoid repeating words ____

5 Match the two parts of the sentences.

1 We'll need to lay ____

2 Tom said he was mopping ____

3 Could you hang out ____

4 I completely forgot to water ____

5 After we finished eating, we loaded ____

6 Ella got up and had breakfast, then made ____

7 He dropped some food and had to vacuum ____

8 Don't forget to take out ____

a the plants in the garden.

b these clothes to dry, please?

c the rubbish, will you?

d the carpet.

e the dishwasher.

f the bathroom floor when I called.

g her bed.

h the dinner table for six people.

GRAMMAR: Articles

1 Match the two parts of the sentences.

1 I would really love a _____
2 Paul said he would like an _____
3 I think I will enjoy the _____
4 We could have _____
5 Esther talked a lot about _____
6 Laura explained the _____
7 Rick told me about an _____
8 Maria described a _____

a book you told us about.
b route to Bill's house.
c drink.
d village in China.
e old friend who was a musician.
f orange.
g politics.
h breakfast before we go.

2 Complete the sentences with the correct article or – (no article).

1 Viv goes to the doctor's twice _____ year.
2 We went to _____ amazing concert last night.
3 I'm a bit scared of _____ dogs.
4 She gave _____ taxi driver a big tip.
5 Patsy has to go to _____ hospital tomorrow.
6 I usually have sandwiches for _____ lunch.
7 _____ Monday is the first day of the working week.
8 They need to go into town before _____ bank shuts.
9 What's _____ name of Pete's girlfriend?
10 My sister is _____ engineer.

3 Read the review and choose the correct sequence of articles, A, B or C.

'Spectacles' review *****

This week we're reviewing Spectacles, 1_____ pair of sunglasses that can take 2_____ videos. 3_____ product is made by 4_____ video and messaging app, Snapchat. 5_____ videos are 6_____ unusual shape: they're round, similar to human vision. Spectacles' 10-second video clips are sent via Bluetooth to users' smartphones.

A 1 –   2 –   3 –   4 the   5 –   6 a
B 1 a   2 –   3 The 4 the   5 The 6 an
C 1 a   2 the 3 The 4 –   5 The 6 the

VOCABULARY: Words to describe materials and clothes

4 Complete the sentences with the words in the box.

silk   fur   casual   wooden   wool   metal

1 I'm an animal lover, so I don't wear _____ coats.
2 You need to polish _____ jewellery to make it shine.
3 It's best to wash _____ shirts by hand.
4 We gave Helga an unusual _____ ring for her birthday.
5 In winter, I wear a _____ jumper to keep warm.
6 Joe packed some _____ clothes for his holiday.

5 Complete the words.

1 My sister is a vegetarian and won't even buy l_____ shoes.
2 You should wear s_____ clothes for an interview.
3 In summer Felipe prefers short-sleeved c_____ shirts.
4 We aren't allowed to wear d_____ jeans to work.
5 Are these trousers too t_____? I think I need a larger size.
6 She didn't buy the skirt with flowers on because she wanted something p_____.

PRONUNCIATION: the

6 ▶11.3 Listen and circle the pronunciation of *the* that you hear. Listen, check and repeat.

1 We need to catch **the** early train.	/ðə/	/ðiː/
2 Where are all **the** other people?	/ðə/	/ðiː/
3 What time does **the** concert start?	/ðə/	/ðiː/
4 Shall we meet at **the** usual place?	/ðə/	/ðiː/
5 Don't forget to bring **the** tickets.	/ðə/	/ðiː/
6 His house is painted pink on **the** outside.	/ðə/	/ðiː/
7 How did you get on in **the** exam?	/ðə/	/ðiː/
8 I've spilled juice on **the** carpet.	/ðə/	/ðiː/

WRITING: Making writing interesting

1 Read David's description of his friend's house and complete it with the words in the box.

> so (x 2)   because   but   although   however   and   also   as well

Michael's house

My friend Michael lives with his parents in a big modern house just outside the city. I think it's an excellent place to live ¹_____ it's really peaceful there, ²_____ it's still easy to get into the city on the bus.

Michael's mum is a keen gardener, and they have a gorgeous garden with lots of flowers. It ³_____ has a large oval swimming pool, where we often hang out at the weekends.

⁴_____ the rooms in Michael's house are spacious, they're still very comfortable. In Michael's room, there's an old leather sofa ⁵_____ lots of soft red velvet cushions. There's a lovely thick rug ⁶_____.

All the rooms have big windows ⁷_____ they're bright and airy. ⁸_____, most of them have thick, black blinds, ⁹_____ you can make the rooms dark if you want to. That's especially useful in the sitting room, where we often watch movies.

2 Order the adjectives to complete the sentences.

1 He owns a(n) _____ bed.
   (huge/amazing/square)

2 Her bedroom has _____ curtains.
   (pale green/silk/fashionable)

3 My house contains a _____ living area.
   (spacious/modern)

4 Their home is full of _____ furniture.
   (old/oak/beautiful)

5 She uses _____ sheets on the beds.
   (Egyptian/white/cotton)

6 I don't like the _____ window frames.
   (horrible/plastic/modern)

7 On the table there is a _____ vase.
   (Chinese/large/round)

8 The dining room has a _____ carpet.
   (blue/gorgeous)

3 Find these words in the text and match them with synonyms a–d.

1 spacious _____
2 gorgeous _____
3 hang out _____
4 get into _____

a spend time
b reach
c large
d beautiful

4 Find two examples in the text of *where* and an example of what you can do there. Then complete 1–4 with your own ideas.

1 Greg's house has a gorgeous long garden, where
   _____.

2 Anna's cottage has an old red living room, where
   _____.

3 Peter's apartment has an enormous square balcony, where
   _____.

4 There is a wonderful modern kitchen, where
   _____.

5 Write a description of a home you like.

- Use adjectives in the correct order.
- Use synonyms to avoid repeating words.
- Use linkers to give reasons and results (*so, because, that's why*), to contrast information (*but, although, however*) or add information (*and, also, too, as well*).
- Include a sentence with *where* and what you can do in a particular place.

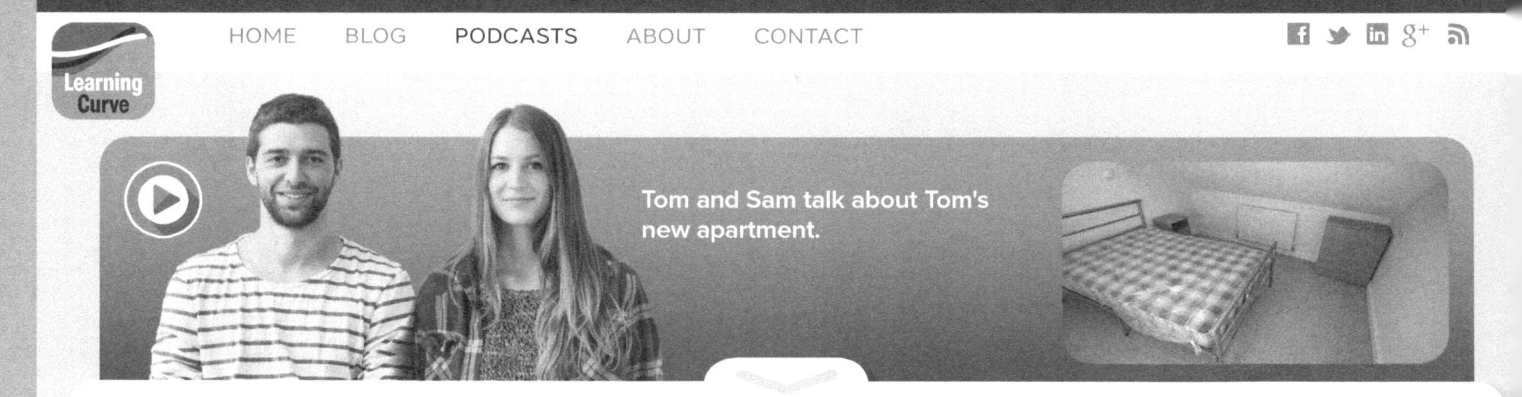

HOME   BLOG   PODCASTS   ABOUT   CONTACT

Tom and Sam talk about Tom's new apartment.

LISTENING

1 ▶ 11.4   Listen to the podcast. Number these things in the order Tom mentions them.

a wardrobe   _____

b sofa   _____

c freezer   _____

d central heating   _____

e kitchen   _____

f duvet   _____

g fridge   _____

h chest of drawers   _____

2 ▶ 11.4   Listen again. Is each statement correct (YES) or incorrect (NO)?

	Yes	No
1 Tom has been in his new home for less than a month.	☐	☐
2 Tom moved in on the coldest day of the year.	☐	☐
3 Tom had to go to bed early to keep warm.	☐	☐
4 Tom was pleased the central heating was soon fixed.	☐	☐
5 Tom hasn't had time to put his clothes in the wardrobe.	☐	☐
6 At the moment, Tom doesn't mind not having a freezer.	☐	☐
7 Tom would prefer different wallpaper in his new home.	☐	☐
8 Tom is confident that Sam will really like his apartment.	☐	☐

READING

1 Read the blog about house-sharing. Tick (✔) the correct sentences, according to the information in the blog.

1 House prices are rising, so more people share houses today than ever before.   _____

2 People often need to share houses, but there can be problems.   _____

3 You need to make sure your new housemate can afford to live there.   _____

4 Feelings are important, but you can take practical steps to make sharing a house successful.   _____

5 If you can't share with someone you know, you should meet them before you move in together.   _____

6 You should make a list of important things about where you are going to live.   _____

2 Are the sentences true (T), false (F), or is there not enough information to decide (N)?

1 Many people have bad experiences with housemates.   _____

2 Mollie's housemate didn't know how to use their washing machine.   _____

3 Jamie liked his housemate's snake.   _____

4 A lot of people move into houses they can't really afford.   _____

5 Becky's housemate was often late with her rent.   _____

6 It doesn't matter why someone left the last place they lived.   _____

7 Daniel didn't like the sort of music his housemates played.   _____

8 If you don't feel comfortable with someone, you should find out where they lived before.   _____

9 Websites can be a good place to find house-sharing opportunities.   _____

10 At a speed housemating event, you can immediately see basic information about people.   _____

Guest blogger Penny explains how to find the perfect housemate.

The highs and lows of house-sharing

You want to leave home, but you can't afford your own apartment. What do you do? Sharing accommodation with other people in the same situation is the obvious answer, but how do you find those people, and how do you know you will get on with them? The internet is full of horror stories – here are a few of them!

'One of my housemates never changed his sheets,' says 21-year-old Mollie Goodman. 'Eventually the whole house started to smell!' 23-year-old Jamie King also had bad experiences. 'In one place I lived, this guy moved in and brought a huge snake with him. Even worse, he filled the freezer with dead mice to feed it!'

Of course, money's another issue. You might be embarrassed to ask someone how they plan to pay the rent, but you don't want to end up like Becky. Her housemate claimed to be an actor, but the truth was that she was usually out of work. Not only did she rarely pay her rent on time, she also thought it was OK to use Becky's shampoo, drink her milk and even 'borrow' her clothes (without asking, of course!).

If you're the person moving into a house, find out why the last person left. Maybe, like Daniel Mills, 24, it was because the others were all in a band together – and rehearsed at home! 'I never got a moment's peace – it was terrible!' he says. If you're the one with a spare room, <u>always</u> ask for references from the people they lived with before. And listen to your heart – if you have a bad feeling about someone, just walk away. But listen to your head as well – even if someone seems great, get an agreement in writing.

Most of us would prefer to live with someone we know, but that's not always possible, especially if you've moved to a new city. Online house-share sites are a good place to start. But one thing everyone agrees on is that you must meet the people you're going to live with face to face before you move in. Because this can take a lot of time, 'speed housemating' events are getting more and more popular – when people with rooms can meet people who want to rent. Everyone wears a sticker showing their budget and where they want to live. It's like speed dating, but with a front door key thrown in!

UNIT 12 People and relationships

GRAMMAR: Defining relative clauses

1 Choose the correct options to complete the sentences.

1 Did you see the photo *who / that / where* I posted yesterday?
2 Is that the neighbour *who / which / where* made the cake for your birthday?
3 That building on the left is the office *which / who / where* I used to work.
4 The woman *where / who / which* usually cuts my hair has left.
5 He loves doing sports *where / that / who* he hasn't tried before.
6 She told me about a restaurant *that / where / which* they do really good vegetarian food.
7 We could meet at that French café – the one *which / where / who* you mentioned earlier.
8 For people *which / who / where* prefer peace and quiet, this hotel is perfect.
9 Is she the girl *that / where / which* you were telling me about?
10 This is the room *that / which / where* most of the meetings take place.

2 Combine the two sentences using a relative pronoun.

1 That's the hotel. We stayed there in May.
   _____
2 I've lost the necklace. Marta gave it to me for my birthday.
   _____
3 Did you hear the joke? Alan told it earlier.
   _____
4 She shouted to the boy. He had dropped his phone.
   _____
5 This is the bus. It goes to London.
   _____
6 Are they going to the club? It opened last month.
   _____

VOCABULARY: Relationships

3 Order the letters to make words that match the definitions.

1 someone who you share an apartment with TALFETAM _____
2 a person or organization that gives people work REPLOYME _____
3 someone who hates another person and tries to harm them MEENY _____
4 someone that you work with GLOECLEAU
   _____
5 someone that you live near to HENIGROUB
   _____
6 a man who is getting married or has just got married MOROG _____
7 someone that you own a company with SUBISSEN TRAPERN _____
8 the brother of your husband or wife, or your sister's husband ROBERTH-NI-WAL _____

4 Complete the words.

1 My father left when we were little, so my mother was a s___ ___ ___ ___ ___ parent.
2 My mother remarried and had a daughter, so I have a s___ ___ ___ ___ ___ ___ ___ ___.
3 She has one cousin living near her, but no other r___ ___ ___ ___ ___ ___ ___ .
4 I don't have brothers or sisters – I'm an o___ ___ ___ child.
5 Sarah doesn't get on with her husband's parents, but I love my parents-i___ -l___ ___.
6 My aunts and uncles all have children, so I have lots of c___ ___ ___ ___ ___ ___.
7 I didn't like the last guy I worked for, but my new b___ ___ ___ is great.
8 Enzo's g___ ___ ___ ___ ___ ___ ___ ___ ___ came to the club – they've been going out for six months.

PRONUNCIATION: Sentence stress

5 ▶ 12.1 Look at the relative pronouns *who, which* and *where*. Are they stressed (S) or unstressed (U)? Listen, check and repeat.

1 Who did you speak to? **S U**
2 That's the town where he grew up. **S U**
3 She must be the woman who works here. **S U**
4 Where are the instructions? **S U**
5 Did she say which train she was getting? **S U**
6 Which jacket looks better with these trousers? **S U**

READING: Interpreting data

A

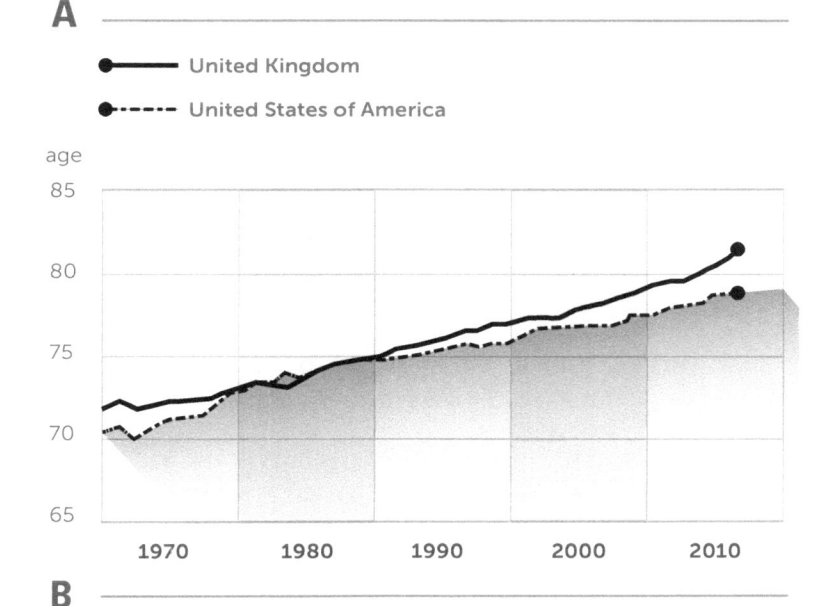

- United Kingdom
- United States of America

B

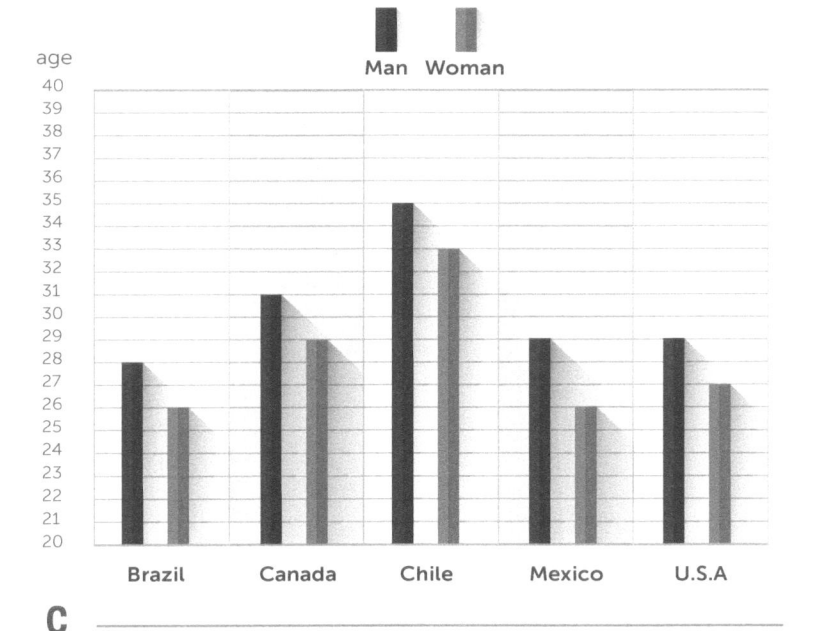

Man Woman

Brazil Canada Chile Mexico U.S.A

C

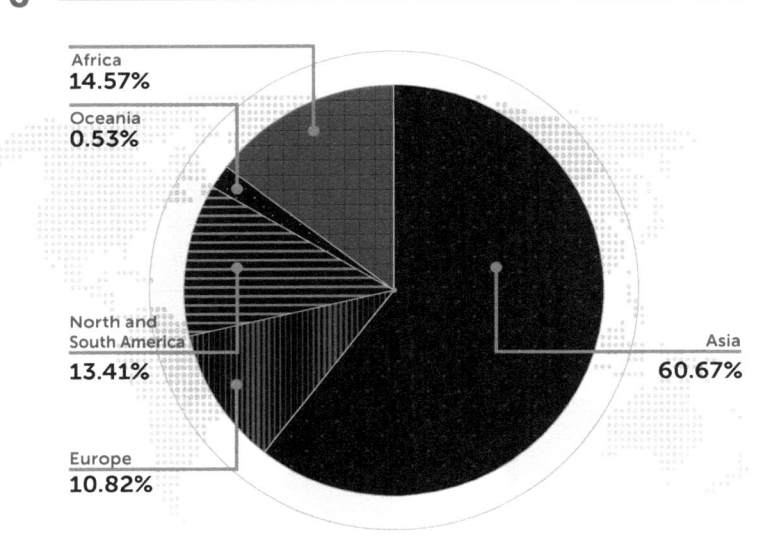

Africa **14.57%**

Oceania **0.53%**

North and South America **13.41%**

Europe **10.82%**

Asia **60.67%**

1 Match the information in figures A–C with three of 1–6.

1 World population by continent. _____
2 Average temperatures by continent. _____
3 Male and female life expectancy. _____
4 Average age of first marriage. _____
5 UK and US population change. _____
6 Life expectancy in the US and UK. _____

2 According to figures A–C, are these statements true (T) or false (F)?

1 Life expectancy in the USA rose by more than five years between 1990 and 2010. _____
2 In 1980, life expectancy for both UK and US citizens was still less than 75. _____
3 The difference between life expectancy in the UK and the USA increased between 1990 and 2010. _____
4 The average age difference between men and women for their first marriage is two years everywhere except Canada. _____
5 Chilean people are older at the time of their first marriage than other nationalities on this chart. _____
6 Brazilian women are the same age as women from the USA when they get married for the first time. _____
7 Asia has the highest population of any continent. _____
8 The population of Africa is about 3% larger than that of North and South America. _____
9 Fewer people live in North and South America than in Europe. _____

3 Choose the correct options to complete this summary of figure A.

Figure A shows that from 1970 to 2012, UK citizens almost always lived slightly ¹*longer / shorter* lives than US citizens. Both groups have ²*increased / decreased* their life expectancy by ³*around / at least* 10 years during the period shown. Between 1970 and 1980, life expectancy for US citizens increased by ⁴*at least / nearly* five years. Between 1975 and 1995, figures for the UK and the USA were ⁵*not at all / roughly* similar. However, for a brief time around 1980, the life expectancy of US citizens was just ⁶*over / under* that of people in the UK. By 1982, life expectancy in both the US and the UK had reached ⁷*at least / almost* 75. By 2012, the average person in the UK could expect to live to ⁸*at least / nearly* 80.

GRAMMAR: Uses of the -ing form and the infinitive with *to*

1 Choose the correct options to complete the sentences.

1 I was disappointed ____ the exam.
   a to fail   b failing

2 Before ____ , perhaps we should have something to eat.
   a to leave   b leaving

3 She's just left the office ____ some lunch.
   a getting   b to get

4 ____ is the best form of exercise.
   a To walk   b Walking

5 I agree there's a problem, although I think it's unfair ____ Enzo.
   a blaming   b to blame

6 It's not expensive ____ on a camping holiday.
   a going   b to go

7 It was impossible not ____ her my secret!
   a to tell   b telling

8 ____ time with friends is so important.
   a Spending   b To spend

9 Not ____ meat can be difficult in some countries.
   a to eat   b eating

2 Complete the sentences with the verbs in the box. Use each verb twice, once in the -ing form and once in the infinitive with *to*.

> earn see discuss eat speak

1 She was too afraid _____ to her boss about the situation.

2 We were both hungry, so we went home _____ .

3 She's certainly keen on_____ a bit of cash.

4 After _____ the matter, we came to a decision.

5 Are you interested in _____ a film this evening?

6 _____ to a room of two hundred people is terrifying.

7 I'd be interested _____ her face when she hears the news!

8 I was delighted _____ a little extra money.

9 Bernando and I met _____ the problem.

10 _____ a lot of sugar is bad for your health.

VOCABULARY: Relationship verbs

3 Choose the correct options to complete the sentences.

1 I met a really nice girl on Saturday and thought I might ____ her **out**.
   a keep   b ask   c go

2 Yasmin and Javier ended their relationship but ____ **back together** last month.
   a got   b fell   c broke

3 Did you know that Ismail and Azra are ____ **married** next year?
   a making   b getting   c going

4 Yusuf and Elin used to go ____ **together**, but they split up.
   a on   b in   c out

5 Azra is **going on** a ____ tonight with a guy she met at work.
   a date   b marriage   c break

6 I've known Pablo for ten years. We ____ **friends** when we lived in London.
   a became   b got   c went

4 Complete the sentences.

1 Although Laura and I are from different countries, we manage to keep in _____ .

2 They met and _____ in love while they were studying.

3 We have similar interests and opinions. Generally, we _____ a lot in common.

4 Nerea is single again. She broke _____ with her boyfriend a week ago.

5 Alejandro seems interesting. I'd like to _____ to know him better.

6 Isabella's great! I've always got _____ really well with her.

PRONUNCIATION: Word stress

5 ▶ 12.2 Match 1–8 with stress patterns a–e. Listen, check and repeat.

1 important ____   a ○ o
2 colleague ____   b o ○
3 impossible ____   c o ○ o
4 except ____   d ○ o o
5 technology ____   e o ○ o o
6 better ____
7 afraid ____
8 probably ____

SPEAKING: Giving thanks

1 ▶ 12.3 Listen to the conversation between Anna and Tim. Which four of these phrases do they use? Number them 1–4 in the order that you hear them.

a Thanks a lot. _____

b That's very kind of you. _____

c Thanks a million. _____

d Thanks. _____

e Thank you so much. _____

f Thanks very much. _____

g I can't thank you enough. _____

h I really appreciate it. _____

i I'm very grateful to you. _____

2 Read the four phrases from the conversation. Match them to the different ways of responding modestly.

1 Oh, I'm glad you like it. It's a really easy recipe. _____ _____

2 Not at all – it would be great fun. _____

3 It's nothing, really! _____

4 Well, not many other people entered, to be honest. _____

   a saying you are pleased

   b saying something isn't difficult

   c saying something is not as good as the other person thinks

   d saying you would enjoy doing something

   e saying something is only a small thing

3 ▶ 12.4 Listen to five people speaking. Choose the most appropriate response.

1 *That's very kind of you. / Thanks.*

2 *Thanks a lot. / I'm very grateful to you.*

3 *Thanks very much. / I really appreciate it.*

4 *Thanks a lot. / I can't thank you enough.*

5 *I can't thank you enough. / Thanks a million.*

4 ▶ 12.5 Listen to four people thanking, congratulating or complimenting you. Use your own ideas to respond modestly.

1 You're welcome. _____.

2 I'm glad you think so, but _____.

3 No problem. _____

4 Thanks. _____

5 ▶ 12.6 Listen to some possible answers to exercise 4.

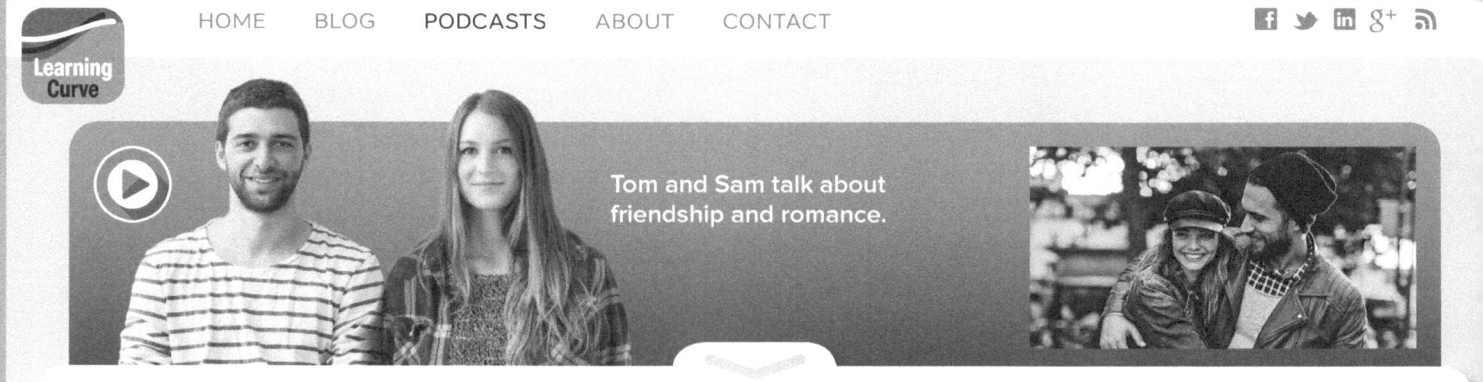

HOME BLOG PODCASTS ABOUT CONTACT

Learning Curve

Tom and Sam talk about friendship and romance.

LISTENING

1 ▶ 12.7 Listen to the podcast. Are the statements true (T) or false (F), according to the speaker?

1 Sophie didn't get on with Marco to begin with. _____

2 Friendships can become romantic relationships. _____

3 What makes a good friend also makes a good partner. _____

2 ▶ 12.7 Listen again. Choose the correct options to complete the sentences.

1 Sophie met Marco at
   a school.
   b university.
   c work.

2 When they were at university, they
   a rarely spoke to each other.
   b never spoke to each other.
   c were in contact with each other.

3 In London, Sophie and Marco fell in love
   a over a period of time.
   b immediately.
   c with other people.

4 Sophie says that when two people start going out together, they
   a can be too honest with each other.
   b usually feel better about themselves.
   c often try to appear better than they are.

5 When Sophie started going out with Marco, she
   a already knew his personality.
   b didn't really like it.
   c found out new things about him.

6 Sophie says that people often choose a partner because
   a they have lots in common.
   b of their appearance.
   c of their honesty.

7 She says that finding someone physically attractive
   a may not be enough in a relationship.
   b is often bad for a relationship.
   c is usually good for a relationship.

READING

1 Read the blog about five people's problems. Complete 1–5 with the words in the box. There are three extra words.

> classmate partners boss flatmate
> neighbours colleagues relative girlfriend

2 Match the advice in 1–8 with problems A–E.

1 You should try to get to know the people you work with. _____

2 It's not a good idea to communicate with this person. _____

3 You might meet someone special through your friends. _____

4 You have to remember that most people are busy. _____

5 There's not much you can do to change this situation. _____

6 You need to think of conversations to have with these people. _____

7 Most people experience this at some point in their life. _____

8 You're unlikely to make friends at work. _____

HOME **BLOG** PODCASTS ABOUT CONTACT

Tom and Sam give some advice about readers' problems.

You have your say

We've learnt so much about other people through writing this blog. Since this is our last one, we've invited our readers to write in with their problems to see if we can give them some advice.

A *We've just moved to a new town. No one speaks to us or shows any interest and we feel we're not welcome. Can you help?*

It's not that your ¹_____ dislike you – they're just getting on with their lives, going to work, seeing their friends, etc. and that doesn't leave much time for you! Why not invent a reason to speak to them? Ask when the next rubbish collection is, or which items you can recycle. People generally like to be helpful and the conversation might lead to other things.

B *I have a small company and my employees get on well. The problem is that they treat me differently. They never chat to me in their breaks or ask me out.*

To be honest, you probably just have to accept it. Your employees may respect you, even like you, but you're not their friend – you're their ²_____ and you have a different relationship with them. If you're short of friends, you need to look in other places.

C *I've just split up with my ³_____ and it's all I think about. I'm OK at work, but at home I don't know what to do with myself. I feel so sad and lonely.*

You probably won't like this, but you have to stop contacting her. The relationship's over – she's made that clear. Keeping in touch will make it worse. Get out and meet new people and you'll stop thinking about her.

D *I'm a single parent. I have great friends, but they're all getting married or have girlfriends or boyfriends and I'm always the lonely guy at the party. Any ideas?*

So your friends all have ⁴_____. It happens to everyone after a certain age. But why aren't they introducing you to their single friends? Why not suggest it? After all, if you get on with them, there's a good chance you'll get on with their friends. One of them may be your future partner!

E *I moved here recently for a new job and I don't know anyone. I'm single and I'm spending all my time alone. I'd love to make friends but I'm shy.*

Come on, don't wait for people to come to you! What about those new ⁵_____? Use your coffee breaks to get to know them. You'll soon find you have stuff in common and the next thing you know, you'll be watching films together!

WRITING: Making notes

1 Read Anup's blog about the best year of his life. Then complete it with reasons and results a–f.

a it had been snowing heavily

b I started chatting to a young woman on the platform

c I was able to travel and see the world

d it reminds me of that wonderful year

e I really wanted to go there

f it was so interesting

This photograph shows me in front of the Taj Mahal in India. The year was 2012 and it was the best year of my life!

I left university that summer but my new job didn't start until the end of the year. That's why [1]_____.
I spent a lot of that time in India, and it was absolutely amazing! I came to England as a young child but I was born in India, so [2]_____. I even brought back some photos of the house where I'd lived with my parents.

In November that year, I finally started my career as a journalist. It was hard work but that's why [3]_____. I was lucky to have a fantastic boss who taught me a lot and it was great to have a job that I knew I was going to love.

And finally, the best thing of all that happened in 2012 was that one day my train was two hours late because

[4]_____. I was bored and fed up, so
[5]_____. Did I fall in love that day? Well, maybe not that day, but I did like her enough to invite her to dinner, and we got married two years later.

Life is still great, but if I need to cheer myself up for any reason, I get this photo out and look at it because
[6]_____.

2 Think about the best year of your life. Write notes about it on the mind map. You can invent ideas – they don't have to be true! You can leave some clouds empty or add new clouds.

3 Read the sentences. Do they talk about reasons or results?

1	2014 was the best year of my life because I got my driving licence that year.	reason	result
2	I wanted to be a doctor, so I had to work hard at school.	reason	result
3	I went swimming every day. That's why I was so fit.	reason	result
4	My boss was away, so I had the chance to do her job.	reason	result
5	I was really pleased because I passed all my exams.	reason	result

4 Write three sentences like the ones in exercise 3. Use *because*, *so* and *That's why* and ideas from your mind map.

5 Write a blog about the best year of your life.

- Write about at least three good things that happened, using your notes from exercise 2.
- Write as many ideas as you can about these three main topics.
- Choose the best ideas then organize them into three paragraphs.
- Include at least three sentences with *because*, *so* or *that's why*.

WRITING: Writing a narrative

1 Read the story about how Ed got a job. Which paragraph (1–4) is missing?

   1 the background   **2** a problem   **3** a resolution   **4** the ending

It was 2014, and I wasn't happy. There I was, 22 years old, with a good degree in computer studies, but I was working as a waiter for a firm that didn't treat its employees well. I kept applying for computer jobs, but companies always wanted experience of working with computers. Without a job, I couldn't get experience, and without experience, I couldn't get a job. The situation seemed impossible.

Then one day, I was working at a party for a large car firm.

Before the guests started eating, the boss wanted to give a presentation. He was using notes that were on his computer, but in the middle of his presentation, it suddenly stopped working.

The boss tried hard to fix the problem, but it still wouldn't work. He started to look nervous. Everyone was waiting for him to finish speaking so they could eat. When I offered to help, he looked surprised, but agreed to let me try. Fortunately, I immediately saw what was wrong and quickly got his computer working again.

2 Complete the sentences with the past simple or past continuous form of the verbs in brackets.

  1 Ed was working as a waiter, but he _____ for a better job at the same time. (look)

  2 Ed _____ to be a waiter. (not want)

  3 Ed _____ enough experience to get a computer job. (not have)

  4 The car firm boss's computer stopped working while he _____. (speak)

  5 Ed successfully _____ the computer. (fix)

3 Find words in the story to complete these sentences. Are they adjectives or adverbs?

  1 Ed didn't feel _____ in 2014.   adjective   adverb

  2 The waiters weren't treated _____.   adjective   adverb

  3 The computer _____ stopped working.   adjective   adverb

  4 The boss tried _____ to make the computer work again.   adjective   adverb

  5 He began to look _____.   adjective   adverb

  6 Ed repaired the computer _____.   adjective   adverb

4 Use these pictures to write the missing paragraph of the story.

- Try to write five sentences. Describe what happened, how Ed felt, and what the situation is now.
- Use verbs in the past simple and past continuous.
- Use adjectives and adverbs to make your paragraph interesting.

WRITING: Writing an informal email asking for advice

1 Read Michael's email asking for advice about a trip. Then number a–i in the order they appear in the email (1–9). The first answer is given.

To: robknight5@openmail.co.uk

RE: Advice

Hi Rob!

^{1}How's it going? Are you still going running every day? ^{2}I'm going climbing in the Himalayas in the spring, but I'm a bit worried about it. That's why I'm writing. I know ^{3}you've been to Nepal, and I wanted to ask you for some advice.

I really love walking, as you know, but I've never done anything like this. It sounds extremely tough and I'm scared ^{4}it'll be too difficult for me. I'm not very fit at the moment. What do you think I should do? Can you give me some ideas about how to prepare, and what I should take with me? ^{5}What's the best way to get fitter in three months?? Can you send me some tips?

Anyway, I guess ^{6}it's good to try new things. Seb told me you've taken up painting – he says ^{7}you're quite good at it!

Do you fancy meeting up for a coffee sometime soon? Then I can ask you some more questions about my trip.

See you later,

Michael

---

a	asking about the person you're writing to	____	f the request for a response	____
b	the ending	____	g mentioning a different subject	____
c	the greeting	____	h the subject	_1_
d	making an arrangement	____	i the details of the problem	____
e	the reason for writing	____		

2 Look at the underlined contractions in the email (1–7) and write the full forms.

3 Complete these phrases from the email with modifiers. Then number them 1–5, from the strongest to the weakest.

1 I'm _____ worried about it.   ____

2 I _____ love walking, as you know ...   ____

3 It sounds _____ tough ...   ____

4 I'm _____ fit at the moment.   ____

5 ... he says you're _____ good at it!   ____

4 Read the problem in the box, then write an email to a friend, asking for advice.

> You have decided to take up a sport or activity that involves a risk.
> Your parents think it is too dangerous and they don't want you to do it.
> You want to do it, but you don't want to hurt yourself.

- Structure the email with a subject, greeting, reason for writing, details, request for response and an ending.
- Use contractions like *I'm* and *don't*.
- Use informal words and phrases like *Hi, How's it going?* and *anyway*.
- Use modifiers like *extremely* and *a bit* to make adjectives and adverbs stronger or weaker.

WRITING: Writing an essay

1 Read the essay about eating meat and put paragraphs A–E in order. Use the linkers to help you (*Firstly*, *The second reason*, *Finally*, *In conclusion*).

A ____   B ____   C ____   D ____   E ____

Should humans stop eating meat?

A   The second reason is the environment. Raising animals for food produces gases that increase global warming. In addition, the animals need to be given huge amounts of water and grain. Also, some studies say that we would need twenty times less land to feed people instead of animals.

B   People have been eating meat for thousands of years and they seem to love it. According to one report, the average American eats around 25 kilos of beef, 27 kilos of chicken and 22 kilos of pork in a year. But is it a good idea to go on like this? I don't believe that it is.

C   In conclusion, I realize that many people love eating meat, but I would say that vegetarian food can be just as tasty. In any case, our world is changing. We are facing serious problems of climate change, obesity and disease, and in my view it's time for us to change too – before it's too late.

D   Firstly, there's the question of the animals themselves. We go to a supermarket and buy a piece of meat in a package, but that meat was once a little lamb or a cute calf. Personally, I love all animals and I don't want to eat them!

E   Finally, there is more and more evidence that eating fruit and vegetables is healthy and eating too much meat is not. I'm worried that diseases such as diabetes and heart disease are becoming more common because many people eat too much, and in particular too much meat.

2 The author talks about three main issues: protecting animals (A), the environment (E) and our health (H). Write the correct letter next to the arguments she uses.

1   There would be more food for people if we didn't eat meat. ____

2   A vegetarian diet is better than eating meat. ____

3   We don't think about animals enough when we eat them. ____

4   Eating meat may be increasing diseases. ____

5   The gas from keeping animals leads to global warming. ____

6   Obesity is a serious problem. ____

3 Read the opinions about 'meat-free Monday' – the idea that you should have one day a week without meat. Complete them with the words in the box, then say if each one is for (F) or against (A) meat-free Monday.

> believe   delighted   worried   say   bad   opinion   personally   good

1   In my _____, we need meat to stay strong and healthy.

2   _____, I feel much healthier when I don't eat meat.

3   It's always a _____ idea to eat more vegetables.

4   I _____ our bodies and teeth are designed to eat meat.

5   I'm _____ that farmers would suffer.

6   I would _____ that vegetarian food can be as tasty as meat.

7   I'm _____ that more people are giving up meat, because I love animals.

8   It's a _____ idea to stop eating meat, because it makes us stronger.

4 Write an essay on the subject 'Everyone should have a meat-free Monday'.

- You can use ideas from exercise 3 or your own ideas.
- Organize your ideas into five paragraphs: introduction, reasons 1–3, conclusion.
- Give examples and evidence to support your reasons.
- Use the linkers from exercise 1.

WRITING: Writing a formal email

1 Read Ben's formal email complaining about his gym classes. What is the correct order of the paragraphs?

1 _____   2 _____   3_____

To: info@gymsforall.co.uk

Subject: Exercise classes

¹*Dear Sir/Madam*

A

In recent weeks, a large number of classes ²*have been cancelled* without notice. ³*In addition to this*, several of the teachers appear to be extremely inexperienced, leading to a real risk of injury.

B

In my opinion, all exercise instructors should ⁴*be checked* regularly to ⁵*ensure* that ⁶*they are* teaching to the highest standards. Please would you let me know as soon as possible how you intend to make improvements to this unsatisfactory situation.

C

⁷*I am writing* ⁸*with regard to* the standard of exercise classes at your gym, which I believe has reached an ⁹*unacceptable* level.

¹⁰*Regards*,

Ben Southgate

---

2 Look at words and phrases 1–10 in the email and write the numbers next to the correct feature of formal emails.

Formal greeting	_____
Using full forms, not contractions	_____ _____
Formal words and expressions	_____ _____ _____ _____ _____
Passives to avoid being personal	_____ _____
Formal ending	_____

3 Order the letters to form nouns to complete the sentences. What is the verb form of each noun?

1 The changing rooms need a lot of i_____.   N T P R M O E V M E

2 Gym members need better instructions to avoid i_____.   R U J N Y

3 Prices are already high. An i_____ is unreasonable.   R E N C A S E

4 Changes to class times have caused c_____.   N F U O N O S I

5 The m_____ should run the gym more efficiently.   N T N A G A E M E

6 We are not given enough i_____ about how to use the equipment safely.   N F R O A M I T N O

7 The d_____ that we were being given dirty towels was shocking.   C O V I S E R Y

8 I have made the d_____ to cancel my membership.   I S C E N O I

9 Your plan to raise the price came as an unwelcome s_____.   R E U R P S I

4 You have received an email telling you that the cost of your gym membership is going up. You feel this is unreasonable because of the poor quality of the gym. Write a formal email of complaint.

- Include three paragraphs: say why you are writing, explain the situation, and say what you want to be done.
- Use the features of formal emails in exercise 2.
- Use the sentences in exercise 3 for ideas.

WRITING: Making writing interesting

1 Read Eva's description of her first meeting with her neighbour. Choose the correct words to complete the text.

The first time I met Davina, I was quite <u>scared</u> of her! It was only the second day in my apartment when she knocked on my door to complain that I was being too <u>noisy</u>. [1]*However / As well / Although* it was two o'clock in the afternoon, she was wearing a pair of pyjamas with a huge old black coat over the top. Her long blonde hair was sticking up all over the place. She looked really <u>sleepy</u>, and really <u>angry</u>, [2]*too / also / however*.

She told me she was a nurse and she was trying to sleep [3]*because / so / that's why* she had been working all night. [4]*But / That's why / And* she was wearing pyjamas. Of course, I apologized. I suddenly realized how <u>loud</u> my music was [5]*because / too / so* I wasn't surprised she was <u>annoyed</u>.

I felt really bad. [6]*Although / That's why / However*, the next day a card came through my door, inviting me for coffee at the weekend. That's when I discovered that Davina is really a lovely person when she's not <u>tired</u>!

Now we get on really well. We sometimes go out together, and I [7]*also / as well / too* look after her friendly little brown and white cat when she goes away. Of course I'm not <u>frightened</u> of her any more, [8]*but / because / also* I never play loud music now!

2 Look at the underlined words in Eva's description and make four pairs of synonyms.

3 Look at the adjectives in these sentences. Write them in the correct columns.

1 My flatmate is a **lovely young Italian** woman.
2 We sat at a **big round wooden** table.
3 Milo had **beautiful long brown** hair.
4 Hannah was wearing a **blue cotton** shirt.
5 Chris has a **fat old black** dog.
6 Karl cooks **delicious French** food.

opinion	size	shape	age	colour	nationality	material

4 Write about the first time you met someone you have a relationship with now, for example a neighbour, friend, colleague or flatmate.

- Use interesting adjectives, in the correct order, to describe things.
- Use synonyms to avoid repeating words.
- Use linkers to give reasons and results (*so, because, that's why*), to contrast information (*but, although, however*) or add information (*and, also, too, as well*).

Richmond

58 St Aldates
Oxford
OX1 1ST
United Kingdom

Printed in Forma Certa Gráfica Digital
Lote:800427
ISBN: 978-84-668-2096-7
CP: 641995
DL: M-10058-2017

Publishing Director: Deborah Tricker
Publisher: Luke Baxter
Editor: Helen Wendholt
Proofreader: Amanda Leigh
Design Manager: Lorna Heaslip
Cover Design: Richmond
Design & Layout: Lorna Heaslip, Oliver Hutton
Photo Researcher: Magdalena Mayo
Audio production: TEFL Audio

Illustrators:
Liav Zabari, c/o Lemonade Illustration Agency

Photos:
ALAMY/Frances Roberts, Nick Baylis, REUTERS, David Taylor, Paul Nichols, Mode Images, M L Pearson, Jeremey Richards, Panther Media GmBH, Big Cheese Photo LLC, Digital Image Library, Sabena Jane Blackbird, www.BibleLandPictures.com, Purcell Team; GETTY IMAGES SALES SPAIN/Thinkstock; ISTOCKPHOTO/Getty Images Sales Spain; REX SHUTTERSTOCK/Solent News; ARCHIVO SANTILLANA

Cover Photo: Jon Barlow

We would like to thank the following reviewers for their valuable feedback which has made Personal Best possible. We extend our thanks to the many teachers and students not mentioned here.
Brad Bawtinheimer, Manuel Hidalgo, Paulo Dantas, Diana Bermúdez, Laura Gutiérrez, Hardy Griffin, Angi Conti, Christopher Morabito, Hande Kokce, Jorge Lobato, Leonardo Mercato, Mercilinda Ortiz, Wendy López

The Publisher has made every effort to trace the owner of copyright material; however, the Publisher will correct any involuntary omission at the earliest opportunity.